TEST ITEM FILE

Laurel Technical Services

EXCURSIONS IN MODERN MATHEMATICS

Fourth Edition

Peter Tannenbaum
&
Robert Arnold

Prentice Hall

Upper Saddle River, NJ 07458

Executive Editor: Sally Yagan
Supplement Editor: Meisha Welch
Special Projects Manager: Barbara A. Murray
Production Editor: Wendy A. Perez
Supplement Cover Manager: Paul Gourhan
Supplement Cover Designer: PM Workshop Inc.
Manufacturing Buyer: Lisa McDowell

ISBN 0-13-031484-6

Prentice-Hall International (UK) Limited, London
Prentice-Hall of Australia Pty. Limited, Sydney
Prentice-Hall Canada, Inc., Toronto
Prentice-Hall Hispanoamericana, S.A., Mexico
Prentice-Hall of India Private Limited, New Delhi
Pearson Education Asia Pte. Ltd., Singapore
Prentice-Hall of Japan, Inc., Tokyo
Editora Prentice-Hall do Brazil, Ltda., Rio de Janeiro

Chapter/ Title	**Page**

Chapter 1: The Mathematics of Voting

Questions 1 through 13 refer to an election with four candidates (A, B, C, *and* D), and with the following preference schedule:

Number of voters	6	3	5	8
1st choice	D	D	A	C
2nd choice	B	A	C	A
3rd choice	A	B	B	D
4th choice	C	C	D	B

(I)   1.   Using the plurality method, which candidate wins the election?

     A)   A
     B)   B
     C)   C
     D)   D
     E)   None of the above

(I)   2.   Using the Borda count method, which candidate wins the election?

     A)   A
     B)   B
     C)   C
     D)   D
     E)   None of the above

(I)   3.   Using the plurality-with-elimination method, which candidate wins the election?

     A)   A
     B)   B
     C)   C
     D)   D
     E)   None of the above

(I)   4.   Using the method of pairwise comparisons, which candidate wins the election?

     A)   A
     B)   B
     C)   C
     D)   D
     E)   None of the above

(I)   5.   In this election,

     A)   B is a Condorcet candidate.
     B)   A is a Condorcet candidate.
     C)   every candidate is a Condorcet candidate.
     D)   there is no Condorcet candidate.
     E)   None of the above

(I)   6.   The ranking of the candidates using the *extended* plurality method is

     A)   first: D; second: C; third: A; fourth: B.
     B)   first: D; second: A; third: C; fourth: B.
     C)   first: D; second: A; third: B; fourth: C.
     D)   first: C; second: D; third: A; fourth: B.
     E)   None of the above

(I)   7.   The ranking of the candidates using the *extended* plurality-with-elimination method is

A)   first: C; second: A; third: D; fourth: B.
B)   first: C; second: D; third: A; fourth: B.
C)   first: C; second: A; third: D; fourth: B.
D)   first: D; second: C; third: A; fourth: B.
E)   None of the above

(I)   8.   The ranking of the candidates using the *extended* Borda count method is

A)   first: A; second: C; third: D; fourth: B.
B)   first: D; second: A; third: C; fourth: B.
C)   first: A; second: D; third: C; fourth: B.
D)   first: D; second: C; third: A; fourth: B.
E)   None of the above

(I)   9.   The ranking of the candidates using the *extended* pairwise comparisons method is

A)   first: A; second: D; third: C; fourth: B.
B)   first: A; second: C; third: D; fourth: B.
C)   first: D; second: A; third: C; fourth: B.
D)   first: D; second: C; third: A; fourth: B.
E)   None of the above

(II)   10.   Using the *recursive* plurality ranking method, which candidate comes in last?

A) A
B) B
C) C
D) D
E)   None of the above

(II)   11.   Using the *recursive* Borda count method, which candidate comes in second?

A) B
B) C
C) D
D)   There is a tie for second place between C and D.
E)   None of the above

(II)   12.   Using the *recursive* plurality-with-elimination ranking method, which candidate comes in second?

A) A
B) B
C) C
D) D
E)   None of the above

(II)   13.   Using the *recursive* pairwise comparisons ranking method, which candidate comes in second?

A) A
B) B
C) C
D) D
E)   None of the above

Questions 14 through 26 refer to an election with 4 candidates (A, B, C, and D), 71 voters and preference schedule given by the following table.

Number of voters	27	19	8	15	2
1st choice	B	A	D	C	A
2nd choice	D	D	C	A	C
3rd choice	A	C	A	D	D
4th choice	C	B	B	B	B

(I)   14.   Using the plurality method the winner of the election is

A) A.
B) B.
C) C.
D) D.
E)   None of the above

(I)   15.   Using the Borda count method the winner of the election is

A) A.
B) B.
C) C.
D) D.
E)   None of the above

(I)   16.   Using the plurality-with-elimination method the winner of the election is

A) A.
B) B.
C) C.
D) D.
E)   None of the above

(I)   17.   Using the method of pairwise comparisons the winner of the election is

A) A.
B) B.
C) C.
D) D.
E)   None of the above

(I)   18.   In this election,

A) A is a Condorcet candidate.
B) B is a Condorcet candidate.
C) C is a Condorcet candidate.
D) D is a Condorcet candidate.
E)   None of the above

(I)   19.   Using the *extended* plurality ranking method, which candidate comes in last?

A) A
B) B
C) C
D) D
E)   None of the above

(I)   20.   Using the *extended* Borda count ranking method, which candidate comes in last?

- A)   *A*
- B)   *B*
- C)   *C*
- D)   *D*
- E)   None of the above

(I)   21.   Using the *extended* plurality-with-elimination ranking method, which candidate comes in second?

- A)   *A*
- B)   *B*
- C)   *C*
- D)   *D*
- E)   None of the above

(I)   22.   Using the *extended* pairwise comparisons ranking method, which candidate comes in third?

- A)   *A*
- B)   *B*
- C)   *C*
- D)   *D*
- E)   None of the above

(II)   23.   The candidate that comes in third place using the *recursive* plurality ranking method is

- A)   *A*
- B)   *B*
- C)   *C*
- D)   *D*
- E)   None of the above

(II)   24.   The candidate that comes in second place using the *recursive* Borda count ranking method is

- A)   *A*
- B)   *B*
- C)   *C*
- D)   *D*
- E)   None of the above

(II)   25.   The candidate that comes in third place using the *recursive* plurality with elimination ranking method is

- A)   *A.*
- B)   *B.*
- C)   *C.*
- D)   *D.*
- E)   None of the above

(II)   26.   The candidate that comes in second place using the *recursive* pairwise comparisons ranking method is

- A)   *A.*
- B)   *B.*
- C)   *C.*
- D)   *D.*
- E)   None of the above

Questions 27 through 31 refer to an election with 6 candidates (A, B, C, D, E, and F), and the following preference schedule:

Number of voters	41	10	10	15	5
1st choice	B	F	A	A	E
2nd choice	A	A	E	F	F
3rd choice	D	E	F	E	A
4th choice	F	C	D	D	B
5th choice	E	D	C	B	D
6th choice	C	B	B	C	C

(I) 27. How many people voted in this election?

A)   5
B)   6
C)   41
D)   81
E)   None of the above

(I) 28. Using the plurality-with-elimination method the winner of the election is

A)   A.
B)   B.
C)   C.
D)   E.
E)   None of the above

(I) 29. Using the method of pairwise comparisons, the winner of the election is

A)   A.
B)   B.
C)   C.
D)   E.
E)   None of the above

(I) 30. Using the Borda count method the winner of the election is

A)   A.
B)   B.
C)   C.
D)   E.
E)   None of the above

(II) 31. Using the extended pairwise comparisons method, there is a candidate that loses every paiwise comparison between itself and the other candidates. That candidate is

A)   C.
B)   D.
C)   E.
D)   F.
E)   None of the above

(I) 32. What is the total number of pairwise comparisons in an election among 21 candidates?

A)   190
B)   210
C) 2^{19}
D) $2^{20} - 1$
E)   None of the above

(I) 33. In a round robin tennis tournament, every player plays against every other player. If 13 players are entered in a round robin tennis tournament, how many matches will be played?

     A) 169
     B) 156
     C) 85
     D) 78
     E) None of the above

(I) 34. $1 + 2 + 3 + \ldots + 99 + 100 =$

     A) 4950
     B) 5000
     C) 5050
     D) 10,100
     E) None of the above

(II) 35. $2 + 4 + 6 + \ldots + 198 + 200 =$

     A) 10,050
     B) 10,100
     C) 20,100
     D) 40,200
     E) None of the above.

(I) 36. "If choice X is a winner of an election and, in a reelection, the only changes in the ballots are changes that only favor X, then X should remain a winner of the election." This fairness criterion is called the

     A) majority criterion.
     B) Condorcet criterion.
     C) monotonicity criterion.
     D) independence of irrelevant alternatives criterion.
     E) None of the above

(I) 37. "If there is a choice that has a majority of the first-place votes in an election, then that choice should be the winner of the election." This fairness criterion is called the

     A) majority criterion.
     B) Condorcet criterion.
     C) monotonicity criterion.
     D) independence of irrelevant alternatives criterion.
     E) None of the above

(I) 38. "If there is a choice that in a head-to-head comparison is preferred by the voters over every other choice, then that choice should be the winner of the election." This fairness criterion is called the

     A) majority criterion.
     B) Condorcet criterion.
     C) monotonicity criterion.
     D) independence of irrelevant alternatives criterion.
     E) None of the above

(I) 39. "If in an election there is a Condorcet candidate, then such a candidate should be the winner of the election." This statement is another way to phrase the

     A) majority criterion.
     B) Condorcet criterion.
     C) monotonicity criterion.
     D) independence of irrelevant alternatives criterion.
     E) None of the above

(I)   40.   An election is held among four candidates (A, B, C, and D). Using a voting method we will call X, the winner of the election is candidate A. Due to an irregularity in the original vote count a recount is required. Before the recount takes place, candidate B drops out of the race. In the recount, still using voting method X, candidate D wins the election. Based on this information, we can say that voting method X violates the

A)   majority criterion.
B)   Condorcet criterion.
C)   monotonicity criterion.
D)   independence of irrelevant alternatives criterion.
E)   None of the above

(I)   41.   An election is held among four candidates (A, B, C, and D). Using a voting method we will call X, the winner of the election is candidate A. Due to an irregularity in the original procedures a new election is required. Before the new election takes place one of the voters changes his mind and moves A from second choice to first choice on his ballot. All other voters vote the same way they did in the original election. In the new election, still using voting method X, candidate D wins the election. Based on this information, we can say that voting method X violates the

A)   majority criterion.
B)   Condorcet criterion.
C)   monotonicity criterion.
D)   independence of irrelevant alternatives criterion.
E)   None of the above

(II)   42.   An election is held among 3 candidates (A, B, and C) using the Borda count method. There are 20 voters. If candidate A received 41 points and candidate B received 58 points, how many points did candidate C receive?

A)   21
B)   38
C)   44
D)   Cannot be determined from the information given.
E)   None of the above

(II)   43.   An election is held among five candidates (A, B, C, D, and E). There are 37 voters. Using the method of pairwise comparisons, A, B, and C win 1 pairwise comparison each. D wins 3 pairwise comparisons, and E wins all the rest. In this election

A) D is a Condorcet candidate.
B) E is a Condorcet candidate.
C)   there is no Condorcet candidate.
D)   there is not enough information to determine if there is a Condorcet candidate.
E)   None of the above

(III)   44.   An election is held among six candidates (A, B, C, D, E, and F) Using the method of pairwise comparisons A gets 6 points; B gets 3 points; C gets $2\frac{1}{2}$ points; D gets $1\frac{1}{2}$ points, and E gets 1 point. How many points does F get?

A)   3
B) $2\frac{1}{2}$
C)   2
D) $1\frac{1}{2}$
E)   None of the above

(I)   45.   Arrow's Impossibility Theorem implies

A)   that in every election, each of the voting methods must produce a different winner.

B)   that in every election, no matter what voting method we use, at least one of the four fairness criteria will be violated.

C)   that every voting method can potentially violate each one of the four fairness criteria.

D)   that it is impossible to have a voting method that satisfies all four of the fairness criteria.

E)   None of the above

(III)   46.   An election is held among five candidates (A, B, C, D, and E) and A gets a majority of the first place votes but B wins the election. Which of the following methods could have been the method used to decide this election?

A)   The method of pairwise comparisons.
B)   The plurality-with-elimination method.
C)   The Borda count method.
D)   All of the above.
E)   None of the above

(II)   47.   An election involving 5 candidates and 30 voters is held and the results of the election are to be determined using the Borda count method. The maximum number of points a candidate can receive is

A)   150 points.
B)   90 points.
C)   50 points.
D)   30 points.
E)   None of the above

(II)   48.   An election involving 5 candidates and 30 voters is held and the results of the election are to be determined using the Borda count method. The minimum number of points a candidate can receive is

A)   150 points.
B)   90 points.
C)   50 points.
D)   30 points.
E)   None of the above

(III)   49.   An election involving 5 candidates and 30 voters is held and the results of the election are to be determined using the Borda count method. Assuming there isn't a five-way tie, the minimum number of points a winning candidate can receive is

A)   151 points.
B)   91 points.
C)   51 points.
D)   31 points.
E)   None of the above

(I)   50.   An election is held for president of the United States. Three candidates are running, a Democrat, a Republican, and an Independent. A certain voter prefers the Independent candidate over the other two, but realizing (because of all the pre-election polls) the race is going to be a close race between the Democrat and the Republican and that the Independent doesn't have a chance, he votes instead for his second choice (his preference between the Democrat and the Republican). This is an example of

A)   the monotonicity criterion.
B)   the independence of irrelevant alternatives criterion.
C)   insincere voting.
D)   stupidity.
E)   None of the above

(III) 51.   The plurality method violates

A)   the majority criterion.
B)   the Condorcet criterion.
C)   the monotonicity criterion.
D)   none of the four criteria.
E)   None of the above

(III) 52.   The Borda count method satisfies

A)   the majority criterion.
B)   the Condorcet criterion.
C)   the monotonicity criterion.
D)   All three of the above
E)   None of the above

(III) 53.   The method of pairwise comparisons violates

A)   none of the four criteria.
B)   the majority criterion.
C)   the Condorcet criterion.
D)   the independence of irrelevant alternatives criterion.
E)   None of the above

(II)   54.   The plurality with elimination method satisfies

A)   the majority criterion.
B)   the Condorcet criterion.
C)   the monotonicity criterion.
D)   All three of the above
E)   None of the above

Chapter 2: Weighted Voting Systems

(I)   1.   How many players are there in the weighted voting system
[20: 7, 5, 4, 4, 2, 2, 2, 1, 1]?

     A)   9
     B)   10
     C)   20
     D)   28
     E)   None of the above

(I)   2.   What is the quota in the weighted voting system [20: 7, 5, 4, 4, 2, 2, 2, 1, 1]?

     A)   9
     B)   10
     C)   20
     D)   28
     E)   None of the above

(I)   3.   The total number of votes in the weighted voting system
[20: 7, 5, 4, 4, 2, 2, 2, 1, 1] is

     A)   10.
     B)   20.
     C)   28.
     D)   48.
     E)   None of the above

(I)   4.   In the weighted voting system [12: 13, 7, 2]

     A)   every player is a dictator.
     B)   there are no dictators.
     C) P_1 is a dictator.
     D) P_1 has veto power but is not a dictator.
     E)   None of the above

(I)   5.   In the weighted voting system [13: 12, 7, 2]

     A)   every player has veto power.
     B)   no player has veto power.
     C) P_1 is a dictator.
     D) P_1 has veto power but is not a dictator.
     E)   None of the above

(I)   6.   In the weighted voting system [100: 50, 50, 48]

     A) P_1 has all the power, P_2 and P_3 are dummies.
     B) P_1 and P_2 have equal power, P_3 is a dummy.
     C) P_1 and P_2 have equal power, P_3 is no dummy.
     D)   all three players have equal power.
     E)   None of the above

(I)   7.   In the weighted voting system [11: 5, 4, 2]

     A)   no player has veto power.
     B)   only P_1 has veto power.
     C) P_1 and P_2 have veto power, P_3 is a dummy.
     D)   all three players have veto power.
     E)   None of the above

(I)   8.   In the weighted voting system [q: 10, 8, 4] a strict majority of the votes is needed to pass a motion. The value of the quota q is

    A)   10.
    B)   11.
    C)   12.
    D)   13.
    E)   None of the above

(I)   9.   In the weighted voting system [q: 10, 9, 8, 1, 1] a two-thirds majority of the votes is needed to pass a motion. The value of the quota q is

    A)   7.
    B)   19.
    C)   20.
    D)   29.
    E)   None of the above

(I)   10.   In the weighted voting system [q: 10, 8, 5], the smallest possible value that the quota q can take is

    A)   11.
    B)   12.
    C)   13.
    D)   23.
    E)   None of the above

(I)   11.   In the weighted voting system [q: 22, 12, 8, 4], the smallest possible value that the quota q can take is

    A)   22.
    B)   23.
    C)   36.
    D)   46.
    E)   None of the above

(I)   12.   In the weighted voting system [21: 10, 8, 5, 3, 2], the total number of possible coalitions is

    A)   16.
    B)   31.
    C)   32.
    D)   63 .
    E)   None of the above

(I)   13.   In the weighted voting system [q: 6, 5, 4, 3, 2, 1], every player has veto power. The value of the quota q is

    A)   11.
    B)   20.
    C)   21.
    D)   22 .
    E)   None of the above

(II)   14.   In the weighted voting system [q: 6, 5, 4, 3, 2, 1], no player has veto power. The largest possible value that the quota q can take is

    A)   11.
    B)   13.
    C)   15.
    D)   17 .
    E)   None of the above

(I) 15. In the weighted voting system [21: 10, 8, 5, 3, 2], the total number of possible sequential coalitions involving all five players is

    A) 16.
    B) 24.
    C) 120.
    D) 720.
    E) None of the above

(I) 16. $\dfrac{100!}{98!} =$

    A) 2
    B) 100
    C) 199
    D) 9900
    E) None of the above

(II) 17. $99! + 100! =$

    A) $199!$
    B) $101 \times 99!$
    C) $2 \times 99! + 100$
    D) $2 \times 100! - 100$
    E) None of the above

Questions 18 through 23 refer to the weighted voting system [25: 22, 12, 6, 3] and the Banzhaf definition of power. (The four players are P_1, P_2, P_3, and P_4.)

(I) 18. The weight of the coalition $\{P_2, P_3, P_4\}$ is

    A) 22.
    B) 21.
    C) 25.
    D) 40.
    E) None of the above

(II) 19. The winning coalitions are:

    A) All coalitions with two or more players.
    B) All coalitions with three or more players.
    C) All coalitions with two or more players one of which is P_1.
    D) All coalitions.
    E) None of the above

(II) 20. The number of winning coalitions is

    A) 15.
    B) 8.
    C) 7.
    D) 1.
    E) None of the above

(I) 21. Which members of the coalition $\{P_1, P_2\}$ are critical?

    A) None
    B) P_1 only
    C) P_2 only
    D) P_1 and P_2
    E) None of the above

(I)   22.   Which members of the coalition {P_1, P_3, P_4} are critical?

      A) P_1 only
      B) P_1 and P_3 only
      C)   All three of the players
      D)   None of the players
      E)   None of the above

(I)   23.   The Banzhaf power distribution of the weighted voting system is

      A) P_1: 60%; P_2: 20%; P_3: 10%; P_4: 10%.
      B) P_1: 70%; P_2: 10%; P_3: 10%; P_4: 10%.
      C) P_1: 40%; P_2: 20%; P_3: 20%; P_4: 20%.
      D) P_1: 25%; P_2: 25%; P_3: 25%; P_4: 25%.
      E)   None of the above

Questions 24 through 27 refer to the weighted voting system [8: 6, 3, 2] and the Shapley-Shubik definition of power. (The three players are P_1, P_2, and P_3.)

(I)   24.   Which member of the sequential coalition ·P_1, P_2, P_3Ò is pivotal?

      A) P_1
      B) P_2
      C) P_3
      D)   All three players
      E)   None of the above

(I)   25.   Which member of the sequential coalition ·P_3, P_2, P_1Ò is pivotal?

      A) P_1
      B) P_2
      C) P_3
      D)   All three players
      E)   None of the above

(I)   26.   In how many sequential coalitions is P_2 the pivotal player?

      A)   0
      B)   1
      C)   2
      D)   6
      E)   None of the above

(I)   27.   The Shapley-Shubik power distribution of the weighted voting system is

      A) P_1: $\frac{1}{3}$; P_2: $\frac{1}{3}$; P_3: $\frac{1}{3}$.
      B) P_1: $\frac{1}{2}$; P_2: $\frac{1}{2}$; P_3: 0.
      C) P_1: $\frac{4}{6}$; P_2: $\frac{1}{6}$; P_3: $\frac{1}{6}$.
      D) P_1: $\frac{1}{2}$; P_2: $\frac{1}{3}$; P_3: $\frac{1}{6}$.
      E)   None of the above

Questions 28 through 31 refer to the weighted voting system [12: 5, 5, 2, 2] and the Banzhaf definition of power. (The four players are P_1, P_2, P_3, and P_4.)

(I)   28.   What is the weight of the coalition {P_2, P_3, P_4}?

      A)   12
      B)   10
      C)   9
      D)   6
      E)   None of the above

(I)   29.   Which members of the coalition $\{P_1, P_2, P_3, P_4\}$ are critical?

A)   None
B) P_1 only
C) P_1 and P_2
D)   All four players
E)   None of the above

(I)   30.   What is the total number of winning coalitions?

A)   1
B)   3
C)   5
D)   15
E)   None of the above

(I)   31.   The Banzhaf power distribution of the weighted voting system is:

A) P_1: 37.5%; P_2: 37.5%; P_3: 12.5%; P_4: 12.5%.
B) P_1: 25%; P_2: 25%; P_3: 25%; P_4: 25%.
C) P_1: 40%; P_2: 40%; P_3: 10%; P_4: 10%.
D) P_1: 40%; P_2: 30%; P_3: 20%; P_4: 10%.
E)   None of the above

Questions 32 through 38 refer to the weighted voting system [25: 16, 8, 6, 3] and the Banzhaf definition of power. (The four players are P_1, P_2, P_3, and P_4.)

(I)   32.   The weight of the coalition $\{P_1, P_3, P_4\}$ is

A)   17.
B)   25.
C)   34.
D)   39.
E)   None of the above

(I)   33.   Which players are critical in the coalition $\{P_1, P_3, P_4\}$?

A)   None
B) P_1 only
C) P_1 and P_3 only
D)   All three of the players
E)   None of the above

(I)   34.   Which players are critical in the coalition $\{P_1, P_2, P_3, P_4\}$?

A) P_1 only
B) P_1 and P_2 only
C)   All of the players
D)   None of the players
E)   None of the above

(I)   35.   In this weighted voting system, which players have veto power?

A) P_1 only
B) P_1 and P_2 only
C)   All of the players
D)   None of the players
E)   None of the above

(I) 36. The winning coalitions are:

A) All coalitions with two or more players.
B) All coalitions with three or more players.
C) All coalitions with P_1 in it.
D) All coalitions with three or more players one of which is P_1.
E) None of the above

(I) 37. The number of winning coalitions is

A) 3.
B) 4.
C) 5.
D) 15.
E) None of the above

(I) 38. The Banzhaf power distribution of the weighted voting system is

A) P_1: 60%; P_2: 20%; P_3: 10%; P_4: 10%.
B) P_1: 50%; P_2: 30%; P_3: 10%; P_4: 10%.
C) P_1: 40%; P_2: 20%; P_3: 20%; P_4: 20%.
D) P_1: 25%; P_2: 25%; P_3: 25%; P_4: 25%.
E) None of the above

Questions 39 through 43 refer to the weighted voting system [9: 4, 3, 2, 1] and the Shapley-Shubik definition of power. (The four players will be called P_1, P_2, P_3, and P_4.)

(I) 39. The number of sequential coalitions is

A) 6.
B) 16.
C) 24.
D) 31.
E) None of the above

(I) 40. Which member of the sequential coalition $\cdot P_1, P_2, P_3, P_4 \grave{O}$ is pivotal?

A) P_1
B) P_2
C) P_3
D) P_4
E) None of the above

(I) 41. Which member of the sequential coalition $\cdot P_2, P_3, P_4, P_1 \grave{O}$ is pivotal?

A) P_1
B) P_2
C) P_3
D) P_4
E) None of the above

(II) 42. In how many sequential coalitions is player P_4 pivotal?

A) 0
B) 1
C) 2
D) 6
E) None of the above

(II)   43.   The Shapley-Shubik power distribution of the weighted voting system is

     A) $P_1: \frac{5}{12}$; $P_2: \frac{1}{3}$; $P_3: \frac{5}{24}$; $P_4: \frac{1}{24}$.

     B) $P_1: \frac{2}{3}$; $P_2: \frac{1}{6}$; $P_3: \frac{1}{6}$; $P_4: 0$.

     C) $P_1: \frac{1}{4}$; $P_2: \frac{1}{4}$; $P_3: \frac{1}{4}$; $P_4: \frac{1}{4}$.

     D) $P_1: \frac{1}{3}$; $P_2: \frac{1}{3}$; $P_3: \frac{1}{3}$; $P_4: 0$.

     E)   None of the above

Questions 44 through 46 refer to the weighted voting system [24: 10, 8, 6, 4, 2] and the Banzhaf definition of power. (The five players will be called P_1, P_2, P_3, P_4, and P_5.)

(I)   44.   The number of coalitions is

     A)   15.
     B)   31.
     C)   63.
     D)   120.
     E)   None of the above

(II)   45.   The number of winning coalitions is

     A)   3.
     B)   5.
     C)   10.
     D)   15.
     E)   None of the above

(II)   46.   In this weighted voting system,

     A) P_3 and P_4 have the same power.
     B) P_3 has twice as much power as P_4.
     C) P_3 has three times as much power as P_4.
     D) P_3 has four times as much power as P_5.
     E)   None of the above

Questions 47 through 49 refer to the weighted voting system [26: 10, 8, 6, 4, 2] and the Shapley-Shubik definition of power. (The five players will be called P_1, P_2, P_3, P_4, and P_5.)

(III)   47.   In how many sequential coalitions is player P_5 pivotal?

     A)   6.
     B)   12.
     C)   24.
     D)   36.
     E)   None of the above

(III)   48.   In how many sequential coalitions is player P_1 pivotal?

     A)   6.
     B)   12.
     C)   24.
     D)   36.
     E)   None of the above

(III)   49.   The Shapley-Shubik power index of player P_5 is

    A) $\frac{1}{20}$.

    B) $\frac{1}{10}$.

    C) $\frac{1}{5}$.

    D) $\frac{3}{10}$.

    E)   None of the above

Questions 50 through 52 refer to the following situation: A committee consists of 6 members (A, B, C, D, E, and F). A has veto power; B, C, D, and E each have one vote. F is a nonvoting member. For a motion to pass it must have the support of A plus at least two additional voting members.

(I)   50.   Which of the following is **not** a winning coalition?

    A) $\{A,B,E\}$.

    B) $\{A,B,C,D\}$.

    C) $\{B,C,D,E\}$.

    D) $\{A,C,D,E\}$.

    E)   None of the above.

(II)   51.   Which are the critical players in the coalition $\{A, B, D\}$?

    A) A only.

    B) B only.

    C) D only.

    D) A, B, and D.

    E)   None of the above

(II)   52.   The Banzhaf power distribution of the committee is

    A) $A: \frac{1}{6}$; $B: \frac{1}{6}$; $C: \frac{1}{6}$; $D: \frac{1}{6}$; $E: \frac{1}{6}$; $F: \frac{1}{6}$

    B) $A: \frac{1}{5}$; $B: \frac{1}{5}$; $C: \frac{1}{5}$; $D: \frac{1}{5}$; $E: \frac{1}{5}$; $F: 0$

    C) $A: \frac{5}{11}$; $B: \frac{3}{22}$; $C: \frac{3}{22}$; $D: \frac{3}{22}$; $E: \frac{3}{22}$; $F: 0$

    D) $A: \frac{7}{11}$; $B: \frac{1}{11}$; $C: \frac{1}{11}$; $D: \frac{1}{11}$; $E: \frac{1}{11}$; $F: 0$

    E)   None of the above

(II)   53.   A player whose weight is bigger than the weight of every other player

    A)   is a dictator.

    B)   is a dummy.

    C)   has veto power.

    D)   is a critical player in every winning coalition.

    E)   None of the above

(II)   54.   Consider the generic weighted voting system $[q: w_1, w_2, ..., w_N]$. Which of the following mathematical statements is equivalent to saying that P_1 is a dictator?

    A) $w_1 > w_2$

    B) $w_1 > q$

    C) $w_1 \geq q$

    D) $w_2 + w_3 + ... + w_N < q$ and $w_1 < q$

    E)   None of the above

(II)   55.   Consider the generic weighted voting system $[q: w_1, w_2, ..., w_N]$. Which of the following mathematical statements is equivalent to saying that P_1 has veto power?

    A) $w_1 > w_2$

    B) $w_1 > q$

    C) $w_1 \geq q$

    D) $w_2 + w_3 + ... + w_N < q$ and $w_1 < q$

    E)   None of the above

(III)   56.   Which of the following is **not** a possible Shapley-Shubik power index for a player in a weighted voting system with 3 players?

    A)   0

    B) $\frac{1}{4}$

    C) $\frac{1}{2}$

    D) $\frac{2}{3}$

    E)   None of the above

(III)   57.   Which of the following is **not** a possible Shapley-Shubik power index for a player in a weighted voting system with 4 players?

    A) $\frac{1}{3}$

    B) $\frac{1}{4}$

    C) $\frac{1}{5}$

    D) $\frac{1}{6}$

    E)   None of the above

(III)   58. A, B, C, D, and E, are the starting 5 players in a basketball team. The coach must choose a set of honorary "captains" for the last game of the season—it can be any number from 1 to all 5. How many different possibilities are there?

    A)   5

    B)   24

    C)   31

    D)   120

    E)   None of the above

Chapter 3: Fair Division

Questions 1 through 4 refer to the following situation: Angela and Ben want to divide fairly the chocolate-strawberry cake shown below using the divider-chooser method.

The total cost of the cake was $6.00. Angela values strawberry three times as much as she values chocolate, while Ben values chocolate twice as much as he values strawberry.

(I)   1.   In Ben's eyes, the piece shown below is worth

        A) $4.00
        B) $4.50
        C) $4.75
        D) $5.00
        E)   None of the above

(I)   2.   In Angela's eyes, the piece shown below is worth

        A) $2.25
        B) $3.75
        C) $4.50
        D) $5.00
        E)   None of the above

(I)   3.   In Ben's eyes, the piece shown below is worth

        A) $2.50
        B) $3.00
        C) $3.50
        D) $4.00
        E)   None of the above

(I) 4. In Angela's eyes, the piece shown below is worth

A) $2.25
B) $3.00
C) $3.50
D) $3.75
E) None of the above

Questions 5 through 13 refer to the following situation: Malia buys a chocolate-strawberry-vanilla cake for $14.00 [Figure (i)]. She cuts the cake into six 60° wedges as shown in Figure (ii).

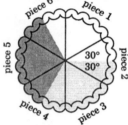

Figure (i)   Figure (ii)

Malia likes chocolate twice as much as vanilla and likes vanilla twice as much as strawberry.

(I) 5. What is the value of piece 1 to Malia?

A) $1.00
B) $2.00
C) $3.00
D) $4.00
E) None of the above

(I) 6. What is the value of piece 3 to Malia?

A) $1.00
B) $2.00
C) $3.00
D) $4.00
E) None of the above

(I) 7. What is the value of piece 5 to Malia?

A) $1.00
B) $2.00
C) $3.00
D) $4.00
E) None of the above

(I) 8. What is the value of piece 2 to Malia?

A) $1.00
B) $1.50
C) $2.00
D) $2.50
E) None of the above

(I)   9.   What is the value of piece 4 to Malia?

       A) $1.00
       B) $1.50
       C) $2.00
       D) $2.50
       E)   None of the above

(I)   10.   What is the value of piece 6 to Malia?

       A) $1.00
       B) $1.50
       C) $2.00
       D) $2.50
       E)   None of the above

Questions 11 through 16 refer to the following situation: Three players (one divider and two choosers) are going to divide a cake fairly using the *lone divider method*. The divider cuts the cake into three slices (s_1, s_2, and s_3).

(I)   11.   If the choosers declarations are Chooser 1: $\{s_2\}$ and Chooser 2: $\{s_3\}$, which of the following is a fair division of the cake?

       A)   Chooser 1 gets s_1; Chooser 2 gets s_2; Divider gets s_3.
       B)   Chooser 1 gets s_3; Chooser 2 gets s_2; Divider gets s_1.
       C)   Chooser 1 gets s_2; Chooser 2 gets s_3; Divider gets s_1.
       D)   Chooser 1 gets s_2; Chooser 2 gets s_1; Divider gets s_3.
       E)   None of the above

(I)   12.   If the choosers declarations are Chooser 1: $\{s_2, s_3\}$ and Chooser 2: $\{s_1, s_3\}$, which of the following is **not** a fair division of the cake?

       A)   Chooser 1 gets s_2; Chooser 2 gets s_3; Divider gets s_1.
       B)   Chooser 1 gets s_1; Chooser 2 gets s_3; Divider gets s_2.
       C)   Chooser 1 gets s_3; Chooser 2 gets s_1; Divider gets s_2.
       D)   Chooser 1 gets s_2; Chooser 2 gets s_1; Divider gets s_3.
       E)   None of the above

(I)   13.   If the choosers declarations are Chooser 1: $\{s_2\}$ and Chooser 2: $\{s_2\}$, which of the following is a fair division of the cake?

       A)   Chooser 1 gets s_2; Chooser 2 gets s_1; Divider gets s_3.
       B)   Chooser 1 gets s_2; Chooser 2 gets s_3; Divider gets s_1.
       C)   Chooser 1 gets s_3; Chooser 2 gets s_1; Divider gets s_2.
       D)   Chooser 1 and Chooser 2 split s_2; Divider gets s_1 and s_3.
       E)   None of the above

(I)   14.   Suppose the choosers value the slices as follows:

	s_1	s_2	s_3
Chooser 1	30%	40%	30%
Chooser 2	32%	32%	35%

Which of the following is a fair division of the cake?

       A)   Chooser 1 gets s_1; Chooser 2 gets s_2; Divider gets s_3.
       B)   Chooser 1 gets s_3; Chooser 2 gets s_2; Divider gets s_1.
       C)   Chooser 1 gets s_2; Chooser 2 gets s_3; Divider gets s_1.
       D)   Chooser 1 gets s_2; Chooser 2 gets s_1; Divider gets s_3.
       E)   None of the above

(I)   15.   Suppose the choosers value the slices as follows:

	s_1	s_2	s_3
Chooser 1	35%	38%	27%
Chooser 2	34%	30%	36%

Which of the following [A), B), C), or D)] is **not** a fair division of the cake?

A)   Chooser 1 gets s_1; Chooser 2 gets s_3; Divider gets s_2.
B)   Chooser 1 gets s_1; Chooser 2 gets s_2; Divider gets s_3.
C)   Chooser 1 gets s_2; Chooser 2 gets s_3; Divider gets s_1.
D)   Chooser 1 gets s_2; Chooser 2 gets s_1; Divider gets s_3.
E)   All of the above are fair divisions of the cake.

(I)   16.   Suppose the choosers value the slices as follows:

	s_1	s_2	s_3
Chooser 1	30%	40%	30%
Chooser 2	31%	37%	32%

Which of the following is a fair division of the cake?

A)   Chooser 1 gets s_2; Chooser 2 gets s_3; Divider gets s_1.
B)   Chooser 1 gets s_1; Chooser 2 gets s_2; Divider gets s_3.
C)   Divider gets s_2; Choosers 1 and 2 divide $s_1 + s_3$ using the divider-chooser method.
D)   Divider gets s_1; Choosers 1 and 2 divide $s_2 + s_3$ using the divider-chooser method.
E)   None of the above

Questions 17 through 19 refer to the following situation: Four players ($A, B, C,$ and D) agree to divide a cake fairly using the lone divider method. The table below shows how each player values each of the four slices that have been cut by the divider.

	s_1	s_2	s_3	s_4
A	20%	32%	28%	20%
B	25%	25%	25%	25%
C	15%	15%	30%	40%
D	24%	24%	24%	28%

(I)   17.   Assuming all players play honestly, which player was the divider?

A) A
B) B
C) C
D) D
E)   The divider cannot be determined from the information given.

(I)   18.   Assuming she plays honestly, what should be player A's declaration?

A) $\{s_2\}$
B) $\{s_3\}$
C) $\{s_2, s_3\}$
D) $\{s_1, s_2, s_3, s_4\}$
E)   None of the above

(I)   19.   Which of the following is a fair division of the cake?

     A) A gets s_2; B gets s_4; C gets s_3; D gets s_1.

     B) A gets s_3; B gets s_2; C gets s_4; D gets s_1.

     C) A gets s_2; B gets s_1; C gets s_3; D gets s_4.

     D) A gets s_3; B gets s_1; C gets s_4; D gets s_2.

     E)   None of the above

Questions 20 through 24 refer to the following situation: Five players agree to divide a cake fairly using the last diminisher method. The players play in the following order: Anne first, Betty second, Cindy third, Doris fourth, and Ellen last. Suppose that there are no diminishers in round 1 and Cindy and Doris are the only diminishers in round 2.

(II)   20.   Which player gets her fair share at the end of round 1?

     A)   Anne

     B)   Betty

     C)   Cindy

     D)   Doris

     E)   Ellen

(II)   21.   Which player is the first to cut the cake at the beginning of round 2?

     A)   Anne

     B)   Betty

     C)   Cindy

     D)   Doris

     E)   Ellen

(I)   22.   Which player gets her fair share at the end of round 2?

     A)   Anne

     B)   Betty

     C)   Cindy

     D)   Doris

     E)   Ellen

(II)   23.   Which player is the first to cut the cake at the beginning of round 3?

     A)   Anne

     B)   Betty

     C)   Cindy

     D)   Doris

     E)   Ellen

(I)   24.   How many rounds are required to divide the cake among the five people?

     A)   3

     B)   4

     C)   5

     D)   6

     E)   None of the above

Questions 25 and 26 refer to the following example: Three heirs (A, B, and C) must divide fairly an estate consisting of two items — a house and a boat — using the method of sealed bids. The players' bids (in dollars) are:

	A	B	C
House	180,000	190,000	200,000
Boat	42,000	50,000	31,000

(I)   25.   The original fair share of player C is worth

    A) $231,000.
    B) $77,000.
    C) $200,000.
    D) $80,000.
    E)   None of the above

(II) 26.   After the initial allocations to each player are made there is a surplus of

    A) $19,000.
    B) $23,000.
    C) $49,000.
    D) $10,333.33.
    E)   None of the above

Questions 27 through 33 refer to the following example: Four heirs (A, B, C, and D) must divide fairly an estate consisting of two items — a house and a cabin — using the method of sealed bids. The players' bids (in dollars) are:

	A	B	C	D
House	195,000	212,000	201,000	182,000
Cabin	45,000	36,000	35,000	42,000

(I)   27.   The original fair share of player A is worth

    A) $240,000.
    B) $120,000.
    C) $80,000.
    D) $60,000.
    E)   None of the above

(I)   28.   In the initial allocation, player A

    A)   gets the house and pays the estate $135,000.
    B)   gets the house and an additional $55,000 from the estate.
    C)   gets the cabin and pays the estate $15,000.
    D)   gets the cabin and an additional $15,000 from the estate.
    E)   None of the above

(I)   29.   In the initial allocation, player B

    A)   gets the house and pays the estate $150,000.
    B)   gets the house and pays the estate $274,000.
    C)   gets the house and the cabin and pays the estate $186,000.
    D)   gets $62,000 from the estate.
    E)   None of the above

(I)   30.   After the initial allocation to each player is made there is a surplus of

    A) $150,000.
    B) $32,000.
    C) $20,000.
    D) $0.
    E)   None of the above

(I)   31.   After all is said and done, the final allocation to player A is:

    A)   the cabin plus $5,000 in cash.
    B)   the cabin plus $10,000 in cash.
    C)   the cabin plus $20,000 in cash.
    D) $65,000 in cash.
    E)   None of the above

(I) 32. After all is said and done, the final allocation to player B is:

  A) the house plus $5,000 in cash.
  B) the house, but player B must pay $155,000 to the estate.
  C) the house, but player B must pay $145,000 to the estate.
  D) $67,000 in cash.
  E) None of the above

(I) 33. After all is said and done, the final allocation to player C is:

  A) $64,000 in cash.
  B) $54,000 in cash.
  C) the cabin plus 24,000 in cash.
  D) the cabin plus 29,000 in cash.
  E) None of the above

Questions 34 through 37 refer to the following example: Four heirs (A, B, C, and D) must divide fairly an estate consisting of three items — a house, a cabin and a boat — using the method of sealed bids. The players' bids (in dollars) are:

	A	B	C	D
House	180,000	200,000	190,000	185,000
Cabin	60,000	50,000	40,000	55,000
Boat	16,000	12,000	18,000	10,000

(I) 34. The original fair share of player B is worth

  A) $62,000.
  B) $62,500.
  C) $64,000.
  D) $65,500.
  E) None of the above

(I) 35. In the initial allocation, player B

  A) gets the house and pays the estate $134,500.
  B) gets the cabin and an additional $15,500 from the estate.
  C) gets $65,500 cash.
  D) gets the boat and an additional $53,500 from the estate.
  E) None of the above

(I) 36. After the initial allocation to each player is made there is a surplus of

  A) $24,000.
  B) $12,000.
  C) $6,000.
  D) $0.
  E) None of the above

(I) 37. After all is said and done, the final allocation to player B is:

  A) the house minus $134,500 in cash.
  B) the house minus $128,500 in cash.
  C) the house plus $6,000 in cash.
  D) $65,500 in cash.
  E) None of the above

Questions 38 through 43 refer to the following: Four players (A, B, C, D) agree to divide the 16 items below using the method of markers.

Each of the player's three markers are placed as follows:

A: immediately to the right of items 1, 6, 12

B: immediately to the right of items 3, 8, 15

C: immediately to the right of items 2, 9, 14

D: immediately to the right of items 2, 7, 12.

(I)   38.   Item 5

    A)   goes to A.
    B)   goes to B.
    C)   goes to C.
    D)   goes to D.
    E)   is left over.

(I)   39.   Item 8

    A)   goes to A.
    B)   goes to B.
    C)   goes to C.
    D)   goes to D.
    E)   is left over.

(I)   40.   Item 9

    A)   goes to A.
    B)   goes to B.
    C)   goes to C.
    D)   goes to D.
    E)   is left over.

(I)   41.   Item 11

    A)   goes to A.
    B)   goes to B.
    C)   goes to C.
    D)   goes to D.
    E)   is left over.

(I)   42.   Item 15

    A)   goes to A.
    B)   goes to B.
    C)   goes to C.
    D)   goes to D.
    E)   is left over.

(I)   43.   Item 16

    A)   goes to A.
    B)   goes to B.
    C)   goes to C.
    D)   goes to D.
    E)   is left over.

Questions 44 through 49 refer to the following: Four players (A, B, C, and D) agree to divide the 15 items shown below by lining them up in order and using the method of markers. The player's bids are as indicated.

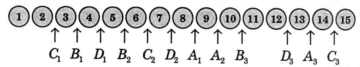

$$C_1 \quad B_1 \quad D_1 \quad B_2 \quad C_2 \quad D_2 \quad A_1 \quad A_2 \quad B_3 \qquad D_3 \quad A_3 \quad C_3$$

(I)   44.   Item 3

    A)   goes to A.
    B)   goes to B.
    C)   goes to C.
    D)   goes to D.
    E)   is left over.

(II) 45.   Item 5

    A)   goes to A.
    B)   goes to B.
    C)   goes to C.
    D)   goes to D.
    E)   is left over.

(II) 46.   Item 7

    A)   goes to A.
    B)   goes to B.
    C)   goes to C.
    D)   goes to D.
    E)   is left over.

(II) 47.   Item 10

    A)   goes to A.
    B)   goes to B.
    C)   goes to C.
    D)   goes to D.
    E)   is left over.

(II) 48.   Item 13

    A)   goes to A.
    B)   goes to B.
    C)   goes to C.
    D)   goes to D.
    E)   is left over.

(II) 49.   Item 15

    A)   goes to A.
    B)   goes to B.
    C)   goes to C.
    D)   goes to D.
    E)   is left over.

(I) 50. Consider a fair division problem involving 5 players. The phrase "a player receives a fair share" describes the fact that

A)   the player receives a share that is at least as valuable as that of any other player.
B)   the player receives a share that, in every player's opinion, has a value that is equal to 20% or more of the total.
C)   the player receives a share that, in that player's own opinion, has a value that is equal to 20% or more of the total.
D)   the player receives a share that, in that player's own opinion, has a value that is exactly equal to 20% of the total.
E)   None of the above.

(I) 51. An estate consisting of a car, a boat, a house and a collection of rare books must be divided fairly among five heirs. This type of problem is called

A)   a continuous fair division problem.
B)   a discrete fair division problem.
C)   a mixed fair division problem.
D)   the method of sealed bids.
E)   None of the above.

(I) 52. Which of the following is a discrete fair division problem?

A)   dividing a gallon of ice cream
B)   dividing a tropical island
C)   dividing a cheese pizza
D)   dividing an antique car collection
E)   None of the above

(I) 53. Which of the following is a continuous fair division problem?

A)   dividing a house plus all the furniture in it
B)   dividing the family jewels
C)   dividing a cream pie
D)   dividing an art collection
E)   None of the above

(II) 54. Joe and Bill want to divide a cake using the divider-chooser method. They draw straws, and it is determined that Bill will be the divider and Joe the chooser. Assuming that each plays the game correctly, which of the following statements [A), B), C), or D)] **cannot** be true?

A)   Joe believes that his share is worth 60% of the cake; Bill believes that his share is worth 50% of the cake.
B)   Bill believes that his share is worth 60% of the cake; Joe believes that his share is worth 50% of the cake.
C)   Joe believes that his share is worth 50% of the cake; Bill believes that his share is worth 50% of the cake.
D)   Bill believes that Joe's share is worth 50% of the cake; Joe believes that his share is worth 60% of the cake.
E)   None of the above

(I) 55. Three players (two dividers and one chooser) are going to divide a cake fairly using the lone chooser method. Using this method

   A) the first division consists of dividing the cake into 2 pieces, the second division consists of dividing each of these pieces into 2 pieces.

   B) the first division consists of dividing the cake into 3 pieces, the second division consists of dividing each of these pieces into 2 pieces.

   C) the first division consists of dividing the cake into 2 pieces, the second division consists of dividing each of these pieces into 3 pieces.

   D) the first division consists of dividing the cake into 3 pieces, the second division consists of dividing each of these pieces into 3 pieces.

   E) None of the above

(II) 56. Sheila, Susan and Rosie want to divide a cake fairly using the lone chooser method. The chooser, Rosie, was determined by drawing straws. Sheila and Susan agreed that Sheila would make the first division of the cake. Assuming that each of them plays the game correctly, which of the following statements [A), B), C), or D)] **cannot** be true?

   A) Rosie believes that her share is worth 1/3 of the cake; Susan believes that her share is worth 1/2 of the cake; Sheila believes that her share is worth 1/3 of the cake.

   B) Rosie believes that her share is worth 2/3 of the cake; Susan believes that her share is worth 1/2 of the cake; Sheila believes that her share is worth 1/3 of the cake.

   C) Rosie believes that her share is worth 1/3 of the cake; Susan believes that her share is worth 1/3 of the cake; Sheila believes that her share is worth 1/3 of the cake.

   D) Rosie believes that her share is worth 1/3 of the cake; Susan believes that her share is worth 1/3 of the cake; Sheila believes that her share is worth 2/3 of the cake.

   E) None of the above

(III) 57. Dave, Doug and Cindy want to divide a cake fairly using the lone chooser method. After drawing straws, Cindy gets to be the chooser and Dave has to make the first division of the cake. Assuming that each of them plays the game correctly, which of the following statements is true?

   A) Dave will believe that the share he ends up with is worth 1/3 of the cake although he may also believe that the shares that Doug and Cindy end up with are worth more than his share.

   B) Doug may believe that the share he ends up with is worth more than 1/3 of the cake although he may also believe that the shares that Dave and Cindy end up with are worth more than his share.

   C) Cindy may believe that the share she ends up with is worth more than 1/3 of the cake and may also believe that the share that Dave ends up with is worth more than her share.

   D) Dave, Doug, and Cindy may each believe that their share is worth more than 1/3 of the cake.

   E) None of the above

(III)   58.   Dave, Doug, and Cindy want to divide a cake fairly using the lone chooser method. Cindy gets to be the chooser and Dave and Doug are the dividers, with Dave having to make the first division of the cake into two pieces. Suppose that $x\%$ represents the value of Dave's share (to Dave), $y\%$ represents the value of Doug's share (to Doug), and $z\%$ represents the value of Cindy's share (to Cindy). Assuming each player plays the game correctly, which of the following statements is true?

A) $x\% + y\% + z\% = 100\%$

B) $x\%$ must be $33\frac{1}{3}\%$; $y\%$ must be $33\frac{1}{3}\%$; $z\%$ must be more than $33\frac{1}{3}\%$.

C) $x\%$ must be $33\frac{1}{3}\%$; y must be bigger than x; z must be bigger than or equal to y.

D) y must be bigger than or equal to x; z must be bigger than or equal to y.

E)   None of the above

(II)   59.   Four investors purchase a piece of land for one million dollars and decide to divide it fairly among themselves using the last diminisher method. The investors are: Aaron, Betty, Carla, and David, and they will play in that order. In round 1, the only diminisher is Carla. In round 2, Betty is the only diminisher, and there are no diminishers in round 3. Assuming that each person plays the game correctly, which of the following statements [A), B), C), or D)] **cannot** be true?

A)   Aaron receives a share that he believes to be worth \$300,000.

B)   Betty receives a share that she believes to be worth \$300,000.

C)   Carla receives a share that she believes to be worth \$300,000.

D)   David receives a share that he believes to be worth \$300,000.

E)   None of the above

(I)   60.   Sue and Tom are getting a divorce. Except for the house they own very little of value so they agree to divide the house fairly using the method of sealed bids. Sue bids 100,000 and Tom bids 90,000. After all is said and done, the final outcome is

A)   Sue gets the house and pays Tom 45,000.

B)   Sue gets the house and pays Tom 47,500.

C)   Sue gets the house and pays Tom 50,000.

D)   Sue gets the house and pays Tom 55,000.

E)   None of the above

Chapter 4: The Mathematics of Apportionment

Questions 1 through 5 refer to the following: A small country consists of four states. The population of State 1 is 44,800, the population of State 2 is 52,200, the population of State 3 is 49,200, and the population of State 4 is 53,800. The total number of seats in the legislature is 100.

(I)   1.   The standard divisor is

   A)   1000.
   B)   2000.
   C)   10,000.
   D)   20,000.
   E)   None of the above

(I)   2.   The standard quota for State 3 is

   A)   24.6.
   B)   25.7.
   C)   26.1.
   D)   26.9.
   E)   None of the above

(I)   3.   Under Hamilton's method the apportionments to each state are

   A)   22 seats (State 1); 26 seats (State 2); 24 seats (State 3); 28 seats (State 4).
   B)   23 seats (State 1); 26 seats (State 2); 24 seats (State 3); 27 seats (State 4).
   C)   22 seats (State 1); 26 seats (State 2); 25 seats (State 3); 27 seats (State 4).
   D)   22 seats (State 1); 26 seats (State 2); 24 seats (State 3); 26 seats (State 4).
   E)   None of the above

(I)   4.   Using a divisor of $D = 1950$ the modified quotas (to 2 decimal places) are

   A)   22.40 (State 1); 26.10 (State 2); 24.60 (State 3); 26.90 (State 4).
   B)   22.97 (State 1); 26.77 (State 2); 25.23 (State 3); 27.59 (State 4).
   C)   22.58 (State 1); 26.67 (State 2); 24.93 (State 3); 27.28 (State 4).
   D)   22.74 (State 1); 26.86 (State 2); 25.12 (State 3); 27.43 (State 4).
   E)   None of the above

(I)   5.   Under Jefferson's method the apportionments to each state are

   A)   22 seats (State 1); 26 seats (State 2); 24 seats (State 3); 28 seats (State 4).
   B)   23 seats (State 1); 26 seats (State 2); 24 seats (State 3); 27 seats (State 4).
   C)   22 seats (State 1); 26 seats (State 2); 25 seats (State 3); 27 seats (State 4).
   D)   22 seats (State 1); 26 seats (State 2); 24 seats (State 3); 26 seats (State 4).
   E)   None of the above

Questions 6 through 15 refer to a country with five states. There are 240 seats in the legislature and the populations of the states are given in the table below.

State	A	B	C	D	E
Population (in thousands)	427	754	4389	3873	157

(I)   6.   The standard divisor is

   A)   4000.
   B)   9600.
   C)   20,000.
   D)   40,000.
   E)   None of the above

(I)   7.   The standard quota for State *A* is

    A)   10.675.
    B)   0.148.
    C)   427.
    D)   11.
    E)   None of the above

(I)   8.   The standard quota for State *D* is

    A)   96.
    B)   96.825.
    C)   97.
    D)   97.825.
    E)   None of the above

(II)   9.   Under Hamilton's method the apportionments to each state are

    A)   *A*: 10; *B*: 19; *C*: 111; *D*: 97; *E*: 3.
    B)   *A*: 11; *B*: 19; *C*: 109; *D*: 97; *E*: 4.
    C)   *A*: 10; *B*: 18; *C*: 110; *D*: 98; *E*: 4.
    D)   *A*: 10; *B*: 19; *C*: 110; *D*: 97; *E*: 4.
    E)   None of the above

(I)   10.   Using a divisor of *D* = 39,540 the modified quotas (to 3 decimal places) are

    A)   *A*: 10.648; *B*: 18.803; *C*: 109.451; *D*: 96.584; *E*: 3.915.
    B)   *A*: 10.675; *B*: 18.850; *C*: 109.725; *D*: 96.825; *E*: 3.925.
    C)   *A*: 10.799; *B*: 19.069; *C*: 111.002; *D*: 97.951; *E*: 3.971.
    D)   *A*: 10.596; *B*: 18.710; *C*: 108.908; *D*: 96.104; *E*: 3.896.
    E)   None of the above

(II)   11.   Under Jefferson's method the apportionments to each state are

    A)   *A*: 10; *B*: 19; *C*: 111; *D*: 97; *E*: 3.
    B)   *A*: 11; *B*: 19; *C*: 109; *D*: 97; *E*: 4.
    C)   *A*: 10; *B*: 18; *C*: 110; *D*: 98; *E*: 4.
    D)   *A*: 10; *B*: 19; *C*: 110; *D*: 97; *E*: 4.
    E)   None of the above

(I)   12.   Using a divisor of *D* = 40,300 the modified quotas (to 3 decimal places) are

    A)   *A*: 10.648; *B*: 18.803; *C*: 109.451; *D*: 96.584; *E*: 3.915.
    B)   *A*: 10.675; *B*: 18.850; *C*: 109.725; *D*: 96.825; *E*: 3.925.
    C)   *A*: 10.799; *B*: 19.069; *C*: 111.002; *D*: 97.951; *E*: 3.971.
    D)   *A*: 10.596; *B*: 18.710; *C*: 108.908; *D*: 96.104; *E*: 3.896.
    E)   None of the above

(II)   13.   Under Adams' method the apportionments to each state are

    A)   *A*: 10; *B*: 19; *C*: 111; *D*: 97; *E*: 3.
    B)   *A*: 11; *B*: 19; *C*: 109; *D*: 97; *E*: 4.
    C)   *A*: 10; *B*: 18; *C*: 110; *D*: 98; *E*: 4.
    D)   *A*: 10; *B*: 19; *C*: 110; *D*: 97; *E*: 4.
    E)   None of the above

(I)   14.   Using a divisor of *D* = 40,100 the modified quotas (to 3 decimal places) are

    A)   *A*: 10.648; *B*: 18.803; *C*: 109.451; *D*: 96.584; *E*: 3.915.
    B)   *A*: 10.675; *B*: 18.850; *C*: 109.725; *D*: 96.825; *E*: 3.925.
    C)   *A*: 10.799; *B*: 19.069; *C*: 111.002; *D*: 97.951; *E*: 3.971.
    D)   *A*: 10.596; *B*: 18.710; *C*: 108.908; *D*: 96.104; *E*: 3.896.
    E)   None of the above

(II)   15.   Under Webster's method the apportionments to each state are

     A) A: 10; B: 19; C: 111; D: 97; E: 3.
     B) A: 11; B: 19; C: 109; D: 97; E: 4.
     C) A: 10; B: 18; C: 110; D: 98; E: 4.
     D) A: 10; B: 19; C: 110; D: 97; E: 4.
     E)   None of the above

Questions 16 through 21 refer to the following situation: A small country consists of four states (State 1, State 2, State 3, and State 4). The total population of the country is 200,000. The standard quotas are $q_1 = 89.9$, $q_2 = 64.8$, $q_3 = 39.6$, and $q_4 = 5.7$ respectively.

(II)   16.   The standard divisor is

     A)   1000.
     B)   2000.
     C)   200.
     D)   100.
     E)   None of the above

(II)   17.   The population of State 1 is

     A)   32,400.
     B)   64,800.
     C)   89,900.
     D)   129,600.
     E)   None of the above

(II)   18.   The final apportionment to each state under Hamilton's method is

     A)   State 1: 90 seats; State 2: 65 seats; State 3: 39 seats; State 4: 6 seats.
     B)   State 1: 89 seats; State 2: 65 seats; State 3: 40 seats; State 4: 6 seats.
     C)   State 1: 90 seats; State 2: 65 seats; State 3: 40 seats; State 4: 5 seats.
     D)   State 1: 90 seats; State 2: 64 seats; State 3: 40 seats; State 4: 6 seats.
     E)   None of the above

(III)   19.   Which of the following numbers can be used as a modified divisor under Adams' method?

     A)   990
     B)   1000
     C)   1004
     D)   1011
     E)   None of the above

(III)   20.   Which of the following numbers can be used as a modified divisor under Jefferson's method?

     A)   990
     B)   1000
     C)   1004
     D)   1011
     E)   None of the above

(III)   21.   Which of the following numbers can be used as a modified divisor under Webster's method?

     A)   990
     B)   1000
     C)   1004
     D)   1011
     E)   None of the above

Questions 22 through 27 refer to a bus company that operates four bus routes (A, B, C, and D) and 100 buses. The buses are apportioned among the routes on the basis of average number of daily passengers per route which is given in the following table.

Route	A	B	C	D
Daily average number of passengers	12,444	36,503	19,581	31,472

(II) 22. The standard divisor is

A) 100.
B) 1000.
C) 10,000.
D) 100,000.
E) None of the above

(II) 23. In this problem the standard divisor represents

A) the daily average number of passengers per 100 buses
B) the daily average number of passengers per bus
C) the number of passengers that one bus is able to transport per day
D) the number of buses required for 100,000 passengers
E) None of the above

(II) 24. Find the apportionment of the buses among the routes using Hamilton's method.

A) A: 13; B: 36; C: 19; D: 32
B) A: 12; B: 37; C: 20; D: 31
C) A: 13; B: 36; C: 20; D: 31
D) A: 12; B: 37; C: 19; D: 32
E) None of the above

(III) 25. Find the apportionment of the buses among the routes using Jefferson's method.

A) A: 13; B: 36; C: 19; D: 32
B) A: 12; B: 37; C: 20; D: 31
C) A: 13; B: 36; C: 20; D: 31
D) A: 12; B: 37; C: 19; D: 32
E) None of the above

(III) 26. Find the apportionment of the buses among the routes using Adams' method.

A) A: 13; B: 36; C: 19; D: 32
B) A: 12; B: 37; C: 20; D: 31
C) A: 13; B: 36; C: 20; D: 31
D) A: 12; B: 37; C: 19; D: 32
E) None of the above

(III) 27. Find the apportionment of the buses among the routes using Webster's method.

A) A: 13; B: 36; C: 19; D: 32
B) A: 12; B: 37; C: 20; D: 31
C) A: 13; B: 36; C: 20; D: 31
D) A: 12; B: 37; C: 19; D: 32
E) None of the above

Questions 28 through 31 refer to a country with six states. There are 300 seats in the legislature and the populations of the states are given in the table below.

State	A	B	C	D	E	F
Population (in thousands)	1756	5822	609	2076	625	998

(II) 28. Find each state's apportionment under Hamilton's method.

A) *A*: 44; *B*: 147; *C*: 15; *D*: 53; *E*: 16; *F*: 25
B) *A*: 44; *B*: 146; *C*: 16; *D*: 53; *E*: 15; *F*: 26
C) *A*: 44; *B*: 146; *C*: 16; *D*: 52; *E*: 16; *F*: 26
D) *A*: 44; *B*: 147; *C*: 15; *D*: 52; *E*: 16; *F*: 26
E) None of the above

(III) 29. Find each state's apportionment under Jefferson's method.

A) *A*: 44; *B*: 146; *C*: 16; *D*: 52; *E*: 16; *F*: 26
B) *A*: 44; *B*: 147; *C*: 15; *D*: 53; *E*: 15; *F*: 26
C) *A*: 44; *B*: 148; *C*: 15; *D*: 53; *E*: 15; *F*: 25
D) *A*: 44; *B*: 147; *C*: 16; *D*: 52; *E*: 15; *F*: 26
E) None of the above

(III) 30. Find each state's apportionment under Adams' method.

A) *A*: 43; *B*: 147; *C*: 15; *D*: 53; *E*: 16; *F*: 26
B) *A*: 43; *B*: 148; *C*: 15; *D*: 52; *E*: 16; *F*: 26
C) *A*: 44; *B*: 147; *C*: 16; *D*: 52; *E*: 16; *F*: 25
D) *A*: 44; *B*: 146; *C*: 16; *D*: 53; *E*: 16; *F*: 25
E) None of the above

(III) 31. Find each state's apportionment under Webster's method.

A) *A*: 44; *B*: 148; *C*: 15; *D*: 52; *E*: 16; *F*: 26
B) *A*: 44; *B*: 147; *C*: 15; *D*: 53; *E*: 16; *F*: 25
C) *A*: 44; *B*: 148; *C*: 15; *D*: 53; *E*: 15; *F*: 25
D) *A*: 44; *B*: 147; *C*: 16; *D*: 52; *E*: 16; *F*: 25
E) None of the above

Questions 32 through 37 refer to the following situation: A country has 4 states. Suppose the population of State 1 is P_1, the population of State 2 is P_2, the population of State 3 is P_3, and the population of State 4 is P_4. Suppose also that the total number of seats in the legislature is M and the standard divisor is D.

(I) 32. The value of D is

A) $\dfrac{M}{P_1 + P_2 + P_3 + P_4}$.

B) $\dfrac{P_1 + P_2 + P_3 + P_4}{M}$.

C) $P_1 + P_2 + P_3 + P_4$.

D) $\dfrac{P_1 \yen P_2 \yen P_3 \yen P_4}{M}$.

E) None of the above

(I)   33.   The standard quota for State 1 is

     A) $P_1 + D$.

     B) $P_1 \yen D$.

     C) $\dfrac{P_1}{D}$.

     D) $\dfrac{D}{P_1}$.

     E)   None of the above

(II)   34.   If q_1, q_2, q_3, and q_4 are the respective standard quotas for the four states, then $q_1 + q_2 + q_3 + q_4$ equals

     A)   the total population $P_1 + P_2 + P_3 + P_4$.

     B)   the number of seats in the legislature M.

     C)   the standard divisor D.

     D)   0.

     E)   None of the above

(II)   35.   If J is the modified divisor used for Jefferson's method, then

     A) J is always less than or equal to D.

     B) J is always equal to D.

     C) J is always greater than or equal to D.

     D)   anything goes: J can be less than, equal to, or greater than D.

     E)   None of the above

(II)   36.   If A is the modified divisor used for Adams' method, then

     A) A is always less than or equal to D.

     B) A is always equal to D.

     C) A is always greater than or equal to D.

     D)   anything goes: A can be less than, equal to, or greater than D.

     E)   None of the above

(II)   37.   If W is the modified divisor used for Webster's method, then

     A) W is always less than or equal to D.

     B) W is always equal to D.

     C) W is always greater than or equal to D.

     D)   anything goes: W can be less than, equal to, or greater than D.

     E)   None of the above

(I)   38.   Which of the following apportionment methods does **not** violate the quota rule?

     A)   Hamilton's method

     B)   Jefferson's method

     C)   Webster's method

     D)   Adams' method

     E)   None of the above

(I)   39.   Which of the following apportionment methods can produce the Alabama paradox?

     A)   Hamilton's method

     B)   Jefferson's method

     C)   Webster's method

     D)   Adams' method

     E)   None of the above

(II)   40.   In a certain apportionment problem, State X has a standard quota of 73.9. The final apportionment to State X is 75 seats. This is called

       A)   a lower-quota violation.
       B)   an upper-quota violation.
       C)   the population paradox.
       D)   the Alabama paradox.
       E)   None of the above

(II)   41.   In a certain apportionment problem, State X has a standard quota of 73.9. The final apportionment to State X is 72 seats. This is called

       A)   a lower-quota violation.
       B)   an upper-quota violation.
       C)   the population paradox.
       D)   the Alabama paradox.
       E)   None of the above

(II)   42.   In a certain apportionment problem, State X has a standard quota of 73.9. The final apportionment to State X is 72 seats. Which of the following apportionment methods could have produced this result?

       A)   Hamilton's method
       B)   Jefferson's method
       C)   Adams' method
       D)   All of the above
       E)   None of the above

(II)   43.   In a certain apportionment problem, State X has a standard quota of 73.9. The final apportionment to State X is 75 seats. Which of the following apportionment methods could have produced this result?

       A)   Hamilton's method
       B)   Jefferson's method
       C)   Adams' method
       D)   All of the above
       E)   None of the above

(I)   44.   Under a certain apportionment method a state receives an apportionment of 42 seats when the total number of seats in the legislature is 234 but only 41 seats when the total number of seats in the legislature is 235. This is called

       A)   a violation of the quota rule.
       B)   the Alabama paradox.
       C)   the population paradox.
       D)   the new states paradox.
       E)   None of the above

(I)   45.   Which apportionment method does **not** violate the quota rule, and does **not** suffer from any of the paradoxes?

       A)   Hamilton's method
       B)   Jefferson's method
       C)   Adams' method
       D)   Webster's method
       E)   There is no such method.

(II)   46.   Under a certain apportionment method state X receives 41 seats and state Y receives 29 seats. Ten years later, the population of state X has increased by 5%, while the population of state Y remains unchanged. Under the same apportionment method, state X now receives 40 seats and state Y receives 30 seats. This is called

     A)   a violation of the quota rule.
     B)   the Alabama paradox.
     C)   the population paradox.
     D)   the new states paradox.
     E)   None of the above

(II)   47.   A father wishes to distribute 16 pieces of candy among his 3 children (Abe, Betty, and Cindy) based on the number of hours each child spends doing chores around the house. Using a certain apportionment method, he has determined that Abe is to get 9 pieces of the candy, Betty is to get 4 pieces, and Cindy is to get 3 pieces. However, just before he hands out the candy, he discovers that he has 17 pieces (not 16) of candy. When he apportions the 17 pieces of candy using the same apportionment method, Abe ends up with 10 pieces, Betty with 5 pieces, and Cindy with 2 pieces. This is an example of

     A)   a violation of the quota rule.
     B)   the Alabama paradox.
     C)   the population paradox.
     D)   the new states paradox.
     E)   None of the above

(II)   48.   A father wishes to distribute 11 pieces of candy among his 3 children (Abe, Betty, and Cindy) based on the number of minutes each child spends doing chores around the house. Using a certain apportionment method, he has determined (based on 703 minues work for Abe, 243 minutes work for Betty, and 54 minutes work for Cindy) that Abe is to get 8 pieces of the candy, Betty is to get 3 pieces, and Cindy is to get 0 pieces. However, just before he hands out the candy, he discovers that he forgot to include 86 minutes of work that Abe did, 12 minutes of work that Betty did, and 2 minutes of work that Cindy did. When he reapportions the 11 pieces of candy using the corrected times and using the same apportionment method, Abe ends up with 8 pieces, Betty with 2 pieces, and Cindy with 1 piece. This is an example of

     A)   a violation of the quota rule.
     B)   the Alabama paradox.
     C)   the population paradox.
     D)   the new states paradox.
     E)   None of the above

(II)   49.   A father wishes to distribute 16 pieces of candy among his 3 children (Abe, Betty, and Cindy) based on the number of hours each child spends doing chores around the house. Using a certain apportionment method, he has determined that Abe is to get 9 pieces of the candy, Betty is to get 4 pieces, and Cindy is to get 3 pieces. However, just before he hands out the candy, he discovers that a neighbor (Dave) has been helping his children with the household chores. Since Dave has worked the same number of hours as Cindy, the father decides to add 3 more pieces of candy and distribute 19 pieces. When he apportions the 19 pieces using the same apportionment method, Abe ends up with 10 pieces, Betty with 3 pieces, Cindy with 3 pieces, and Dave with 3 pieces. This is an example of

     A)   a violation of the quota rule.
     B)   the Alabama paradox.
     C)   the population paradox.
     D)   the new states paradox.
     E)   None of the above

(II) 50.   A father wishes to distribute 16 pieces of candy among his 3 children (Abe, Betty, and Cindy) based on the number of hours each child spends doing chores around the house. Based on the time each child spent doing chores, Abe deserves 7.8 pieces of candy, Betty deserves 4.8 pieces, and Cindy deserves 3.4 pieces. Using a certain apportionment method, Abe ends up with 9 pieces of the candy, Betty ends up with 4 pieces, and Cindy ends up with 3 pieces. This is an example of

A)   a violation of the quota rule.
B)   the Alabama paradox.
C)   the population paradox.
D)   the new states paradox.
E)   None of the above

Chapter 5: Euler Circuits

Questions 1 through 6 refer to the following graph.

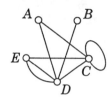

(I)　1.　Vertex A is adjacent to

　　A)　every other vertex.
　　B)　vertex B and vertex E only.
　　C)　vertex C and vertex D only.
　　D)　vertex D only.
　　E)　None of the above

(I)　2.　The degree of vertex D is

　　A)　5.
　　B)　$4\frac{1}{2}$.
　　C)　4.
　　D)　3.
　　E)　None of the above

(I)　3.　The degree of vertex C is

　　A)　2.
　　B)　3.
　　C)　4.
　　D)　5.
　　E)　None of the above

(I)　4.　Which of the following [A), B), C), or D)] is **not** a path from vertex D to vertex A?

　　A)　D, C, A
　　B)　D, C, C, A
　　C)　D, E, C, D, A
　　D)　D, E, D, C, C, A
　　E)　All of the above are paths from D to A.

(I)　5.　Which of the following [A), B), C), or D)] is **not** a circuit in the graph?

　　A)　C, A, D, C
　　B)　A, D, E, C, A
　　C)　A, D, C, D, E, D, A
　　D)　E, D, C, C, E
　　E)　All of the above are circuits in the graph.

(I)　6.　Which of the following is a bridge of the graph?

　　A)　CC
　　B)　BD
　　C)　AD
　　D)　EC
　　E)　None of the above

Questions 7 through 10 refer to the graph with vertices A, B, C, D, E and edges AB, AE, BD, BE, CD, and DD.

(I)   7.   The degree of vertex E is

A)   0.
B)   1.
C)   2.
D)   3.
E)   None of the above

(I)   8.   The degree of vertex D is

A)   1.
B)   2.
C)   3.
D)   4.
E)   None of the above

(I)   9.   The bridges of the graph are

A) BD, CD, and DD.
B) AB, BD, and CD.
C) BD and CD.
D) BD only.
E)   None of the above

(I)   10.   Which of the following [A), B), C), or D)] is **not** a circuit of the graph?

A) D, D
B) A, B, E, A
C) E, B, A, E
D) A, B, D, D, B, E, A
E)   None of the above

Questions 11 through 16 refer to the following four graphs.

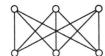 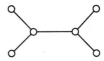

Graph 1   Graph 2   Graph 3   Graph 4

(I)   11.   Which graph has an Euler circuit?

A)   Graph 1
B)   Graph 2
C)   Graph 3
D)   Graph 4
E)   None of the above

(I)   12.   Which graphs are disconnected?

A)   Graph 1 and Graph 4
B)   Graph 2 only
C)   Graph 3 only
D)   Graph 2 and Graph 3
E)   None of the above

(I)   13.   Which graph has 3 components?

A)   Graph 1
B)   Graph 2
C)   Graph 3
D)   Graph 4
E)   None of the above

(I)   14.   In which graph is it true that every edge is a bridge?

A)   Graph 1
B)   Graph 2
C)   Graph 3
D)   Graph 4
E)   None of the above

(I)   15.   Which graph describes the following situation: 3 boys and 3 girls go to a dance and every boy dances with every girl.

A)   Graph 1
B)   Graph 2
C)   Graph 3
D)   Graph 4
E)   None of the above

(I)   16.   Which graph has no circuits?

A)   Graph 1
B)   Graph 2
C)   Graph 3
D)   Graph 4
E)   None of the above

Questions 17 and 18 refer to the following three graphs.

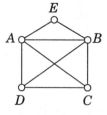   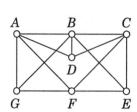   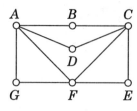

Graph 1   Graph 2   Graph 3

(I)   17.   Which of the graphs has an Euler circuit?

A)   Graph 1 only
B)   Graph 2 only
C)   Graph 3 only
D)   Graphs 1 and 3
E)   None of the above

(I)   18.   Which of the graphs has an Euler path but no Euler circuit?

A)   Graph 1 only
B)   Graph 2 only
C)   Graph 3 only
D)   Graphs 1 and 2
E)   None of the above

Questions 19 and 20 refer to the following three drawings.

 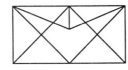 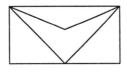

Fig. 1   Fig. 2   Fig. 3

(I)   19.   Which of the drawings has an open unicursal tracing?

A)   Fig. 1 only
B)   Fig. 2 only
C)   Fig. 3 only
D)   Fig. 1 and Fig. 3
E)   None of the above

(I)   20.   Which of the drawings has a closed unicursal tracing?

A)   Fig. 1 only
B)   Fig. 2 only
C)   Fig. 3 only
D)   Fig. 1 and Fig. 3
E)   None of the above

Questions 21 through 23 refer to the following situation: An undercover police officer is assigned the job of walking once a night each of the 48 blocks of a certain section of town described by the street grid shown below. The walk starts and ends at A. The officer wants to minimize the total number of blocks he has to walk each night.

A

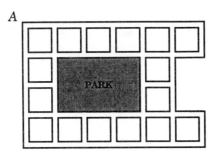

(I)   21.   How many vertices of odd degree are there in the graph representing this problem?

A)   18
B)   20
C)   22
D)   24
E)   None of the above

(II)   22.   An optimal eulerization of the graph representing this problem can be obtained by adding

A)   9 edges.
B)   10 edges.
C)   11 edges.
D)   12 edges.
E)   None of the above

(II)   23.   Suppose that it takes the officer 5 minutes to walk a block. In an optimal trip, the officer will cover the entire neighborhood in

    A)   4 hours and 45 minutes.
    B)   4 hours and 50 minutes.
    C)   5 hours.
    D)   5 hours and 10 minutes.
    E)   None of the above

Questions 24 through 26 refer to the following situation: A city crew must paint the median divider along each of the 48 streets in the neighborhood shown below (starting and ending at *A*). The foreman wants to organize the route in the most efficient possible way.

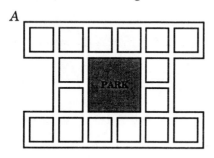

(I)   24.   The number of vertices of odd degree in the graph that models this problem is

    A)   16.
    B)   12.
    C)   8.
    D)   4.
    E)   None of the above

(II)   25.   An optimal eulerization of the graph that models this problem can be obtained by adding

    A)   six edges.
    B)   eight edges.
    C)   twelve edges.
    D)   sixteen edges.
    E)   None of the above

(II)   26.   In an optimal trip through the neighborhood the crew will travel a total of

    A)   64 blocks
    B)   58 blocks.
    C)   56 blocks.
    D)   48 blocks.
    E)   None of the above

Questions 27 through 29 refer to the following situation: A city crew must paint the median divider along each of the 48 streets in the neighborhood shown below (starting and ending at *A*). The foreman wants to organize the route in the most efficient possible way.

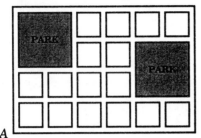

(I)   27.   The number of vertices of odd degree in the graph that models this problem is

    A)   20.
    B)   18.
    C)   16.
    D)   14.
    E)   None of the above

(II)   28.   An optimal eulerization of the graph that models this problem can be obtained by adding

    A)   ten edges.
    B)   twelve edges.
    C)   fourteen edges.
    D)   sixteen edges.
    E)   None of the above

(II)   29.   In an optimal trip through the neighborhood the crew will travel a total of

    A)   60 blocks
    B)   62 blocks.
    C)   64 blocks.
    D)   66 blocks.
    E)   None of the above

Questions 30 through 32 refer to the following situation: A city crew must paint the median divider along each of the 48 streets in the neighborhood shown below (starting and ending at *A*). The foreman wants to organize the route in the most efficient possible way.

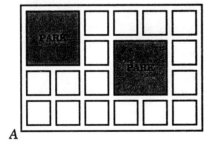

(I)   30.   The number of vertices of odd degree in the graph that models this problem is

    A)   20.
    B)   18.
    C)   16.
    D)   14.
    E)   None of the above

(II) 31. An optimal eulerization of the graph that models this problem can be obtained by
           adding

           A) ten edges.
           B) twelve edges.
           C) fourteen edges.
           D) sixteen edges.
           E) None of the above

(II) 32. In an optimal trip through the neighborhood the crew will travel a total of

           A) 60 blocks
           B) 62 blocks.
           C) 64 blocks.
           D) 66 blocks.
           E) None of the above

Questions 33 through 38 refer to the following situation: In a certain city there is a river
running through the middle of the city. There are three islands and nine bridges as shown in
the figure.

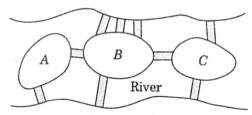

North Bank

South Bank

(I) 33. A graph that appropriately models this situation would have

          A) 3 vertices and 9 edges.
          B) 9 vertices and 3 edges.
          C) 9 vertices and 5 edges.
          D) 5 vertices and 9 edges.
          E) None of the above

(I) 34. In the graph that models this situation, the degree of the vertex that represents
          island A is

          A) 1.
          B) 2.
          C) 3.
          D) 4.
          E) None of the above

(I) 35. In the graph that models this situation, the degree of the vertex that represents
          island B is

          A) 3.
          B) 4.
          C) 5.
          D) 6.
          E) None of the above

(I)   36.   In the graph that models this situation, the degree of the vertex that represents the South Bank is

     A)   1.
     B)   2.
     C)   3.
     D)   4.
     E)   None of the above

(II)   37.   It is possible to take a walk through this town, starting on the South Bank, crossing each bridge once (and only once) and ending

     A)   on island C.
     B)   on island B.
     C)   on the North Bank.
     D)   back on the South Bank.
     E)   None of the above

(II)   38.   Suppose that there is a crossing charge of $1.00 every time one crosses a bridge. A tourist wants to start on the South Bank, stroll across each of the bridges at least once, and return to her hotel on the South Bank at the end of the trip. What is the cheapest possible cost of such a trip?

     A) $9
     B) $10
     C) $18
     D)   Such a trip is impossible.
     E)   None of the above

Questions 39 through 42 refer to the following situation: In a certain city there is a river running through the middle of the city. There are three islands and nine bridges as shown in the figure.

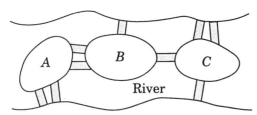

North Bank

A B C

River

South Bank

(I)   39.   A graph that appropriately models this situation would have

     A)   3 vertices and 9 edges.
     B)   9 vertices and 3 edges.
     C)   9 vertices and 5 edges.
     D)   5 vertices and 9 edges.
     E)   None of the above

(I)   40.   In the graph that models this situation, the degree of the vertex that represents the North Bank is

     A)   1.
     B)   2.
     C)   3.
     D)   4.
     E)   None of the above

(II)   41.   It is possible to take a walk through this town, starting on the South Bank, crossing each bridge once (and only once) and ending

    A)   on island C.
    B)   on island B.
    C)   on the North Bank.
    D)   back on the South Bank.
    E)   None of the above

(II)   42.   Suppose that there is a crossing charge of $1.00 every time one crosses a bridge. A tourist wants to start on the South Bank, stroll across each of the bridges at least once, and return to her hotel on the South Bank at the end of the trip. What is the cheapest possible cost of such a trip?

    A) $9
    B) $10
    C) $11
    D) $12
    E)   None of the above

(I)   43.   A graph has an Euler circuit if

    A)   it is connected and has an even number of edges.
    B)   it is connected and has an even number of vertices.
    C)   it is connected and every vertex has even degree.
    D)   every vertex has even degree.
    E)   None of the above

(I)   44.   A graph without an Euler circuit but with an Euler path

    A)   must be connected and every vertex must have even degree.
    B)   must be connected and have exactly one vertex of odd degree.
    C)   must be connected and every vertex must have odd degree.
    D)   must be connected and have exactly two vertices of odd degree.
    E)   None of the above

(I)   45.   A graph with 11 vertices has an Euler path but no Euler circuit. The graph must have

    A)   11 vertices of even degree.
    B)   2 vertices of even degree and 9 vertices of odd degree.
    C)   2 vertices of odd degree and 9 vertices of even degree.
    D)   11 vertices of odd degree.
    E)   None of the above

(II)   46.   A graph has 15 edges. The sum of the degrees of all the vertices of this graph is

    A)   15.
    B)   45.
    C)   90.
    D)   not possible to determine from the information given.
    E)   None of the above

(II)   47.   A graph has six vertices—two vertices of degree 4, two vertices of degree 3, and two vertices of degree 2. The number of edges in the graph is

    A)   9.
    B)   8.
    C)   6.
    D)   5.
    E)   None of the above

(II) 48. If a graph has six vertices and M is the number of vertices of odd degree, then M **cannot** be

A) 0.
B) 3.
C) 4.
D) 6.
E) None of the above

(II) 49. The basic rule in Fleury's algorithm is

A) never travel across a bridge of the original graph.
B) only travel across a bridge of the original graph if there is no other alternative.
C) never travel across a bridge of the untraveled part of the graph.
D) only travel across a bridge of the untraveled part of the graph if there is no other alternative.
E) None of the above

Chapter 6: The Traveling-Salesman Problem

(I)   1.   The number of edges in K_{15} is

      A)   15.
      B)   105.
      C)   210.
      D)   15!.
      E)   None of the above

(I)   2.   The number of Hamilton circuits in K_{15} is

      A)   15.
      B) $\dfrac{15 \times 14}{2}$.
      C)   14!.
      D)   15!.
      E)   None of the above

(I)   3.   The number of edges in the complete graph with 100 vertices is

      A)   99.
      B) $\dfrac{99 \times 100}{2}$.
      C) $\dfrac{100 \times 101}{2}$.
      D)   100!.
      E)   None of the above

(II)   4.   The number of Hamilton circuits in the complete graph with 10 vertices is

      A)   in the hundreds.
      B)   in the hundreds of thousands.
      C)   in the millions.
      D)   more than a billion.
      E)   None of the above

(I)   5. $n! =$

      A) $1 + 2 + 3 + \ldots + n$
      B) $\frac{1}{2} n(n-1)$
      C) $n + 1$
      D) $1 ¥ 2 ¥ 3 ¥ \ldots ¥ n$
      E)   None of the above

(I)   6. $\dfrac{50!}{49!} =$

      A)   1
      B)   49
      C)   50
      D)   51
      E)   None of the above

(II)   7.   If $99! \approx 10^{156}$, which of the following numbers most closely approximates 100!?

    A) $10^{156} + 1$
    B) $10^{156} + 100$
    C) 10^{157}
    D) 10^{158}
    E)   None of the above

(I)   8.   In a complete graph with 12 vertices (A through L), the total number of Hamilton circuits (including mirror-image circuits) that start at vertex A is

    A)   10!
    B)   11!
    C)   12!
    D)   13!
    E)   None of the above

(III)   9.   In a complete graph with 12 vertices (A through L), the total number of Hamilton paths that start at vertex A and end at vertex L is

    A)   10!
    B)   11!
    C)   12!
    D)   13!
    E)   None of the above

(II)   10.   The following graph

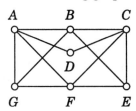

    A)   has no Hamilton circuit.
    B)   has a single Hamilton circuit (and its mirror-image circuit).
    C)   has several Hamilton circuits, none of which contain the edge BC.
    D)   has several Hamilton circuits, all of which contain the edge AD.
    E)   None of the above

(II)   11.   The following graph

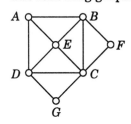

    A)   has no Hamilton circuit.
    B)   has a single Hamilton circuit (and its mirror-image circuit).
    C)   has several Hamilton circuits, none of which contain the edge BC.
    D)   has several Hamilton circuits, all of which contain the edge AD.
    E)   None of the above

(II)   12.   The following graph

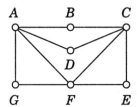

A)   has no Hamilton path.
B)   has a Hamilton path that starts at G and ends at E.
C)   has a Hamilton path that starts at D and ends at G.
D)   has a Hamilton path that starts at G and ends at F.
E)   None of the above

(II)   13.   The following graph

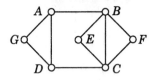

A)   has no Hamilton path.
B)   has a Hamilton path that starts at A and ends at B.
C)   has a Hamilton path that starts at D and ends at G.
D)   has a Hamilton path that starts at G and ends at F.
E)   None of the above

Questions 14 through 17 refer to the following situation: A delivery truck must deliver furniture to 4 different locations ($A, B, C,$ and D). The trip must start and end at A. The graph below shows the distances between locations (in miles). We want to minimize the total distance traveled.

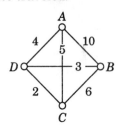

(I)   14.   The nearest neighbor algorithm applied to the graph yields the following solution:

A) A, D, B, C, A.
B) A, D, C, B, A.
C) A, C, B, D, A.
D) A, B, D, C, A.
E)   None of the above

(I)   15.   The cheapest link algorithm applied to the graph yields the following solution:

A) A, D, B, C, A.
B) A, D, C, B, A.
C) A, C, B, D, A.
D) A, B, D, C, A.
E)   None of the above

(I)   16.   The repetitive nearest neighbor algorithm applied to the graph yields the following solution:

    A) A, D, B, C, A.
    B) A, D, C, B, A.
    C) A, C, B, D, A.
    D) A, B, D, C, A.
    E)   None of the above

(I)   17.   An optimal solution to this problem is given by

    A) A, D, C, B, A.
    B) A, C, B, D, A.
    C) A, B, D, C, A.
    D) A, C, D, B, A.
    E)   None of the above

Questions 18 through 21 refer to the following situation: A garbage truck must pick up garbage at 4 different dump sites ($A, B, C,$ and D) as shown on the graph below, starting and ending at A. The numbers on the edges represent distances between locations (in miles). The truck driver wants to minimize the total length of the trip.

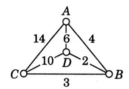

(I)   18.   The nearest neighbor algorithm applied to the graph yields the following solution:

    A) A, C, B, D, A.
    B) A, D, C, B, A.
    C) A, B, D, C, A.
    D) A, B, C, D, A.
    E)   None of the above

(I)   19.   The cheapest link algorithm applied to the graph yields the following solution:

    A) A, C, B, D, A.
    B) A, D, C, B, A.
    C) A, B, D, C, A.
    D) A, B, C, D, A.
    E)   None of the above

(II)   20.   The repetitive nearest neighbor algorithm applied to the graph yields the following solution:

    A) A, C, B, D, A.
    B) A, D, C, B, A.
    C) A, B, D, C, A.
    D) A, B, C, D, A.
    E)   None of the above

(I)   21.   An optimal solution to this problem is given by

    A) A, C, B, D, A.
    B) A, D, C, B, A.
    C) A, B, D, C, A.
    D) A, D, B, C, A.
    E)   None of the above

Questions 22 through 25 refer to the following situation: A delivery truck must deliver packages to 5 different store locations (*A*, *B*, *C*, *D*, and *E*). The trip must start and end at *A*. The graph below shows the distances between locations (in miles). We want to minimize the total distance traveled.

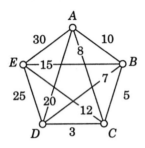

(II) 22.   How many different Hamilton circuits would we have to check if we use the brute force algorithm? (Do not count the same circuit traveled backward.)

A)   4
B)   12
C)   30
D)   60
E)   None of the above

(I) 23.   The nearest neighbor algorithm applied to the graph yields the following solution:

A)   *A, B, C, D, E, A*.
B)   *A, C, D, B, E, A*.
C)   *A, D, B, E, C, A*.
D)   *A, E, C, D, B, A*.
E)   None of the above

(I) 24.   The cheapest link algorithm applied to the graph yields the following solution:

A)   *A, B, C, D, E, A*.
B)   *A, C, D, B, E, A*.
C)   *A, D, B, E, C, A*.
D)   *A, E, C, D, B, A*.
E)   None of the above

(II) 25.   The repetitive nearest neighbor algorithm applied to the graph yields the following solution:

A)   *A, B, C, D, E, A*.
B)   *A, C, D, B, E, A*.
C)   *A, D, B, E, C, A*.
D)   *A, E, C, D, B, A*.
E)   None of the above

Questions 26 through 28 refer to the following situation: A delivery truck must deliver packages to 5 different store locations (*A*, *B*, *C*, *D*, and *E*). The trip must start and end at *D*. The graph below shows the distances between locations (in miles). We want to minimize the total distance traveled.

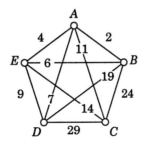

(I) 26. The nearest neighbor algorithm applied to the graph yields the following solution:

   A) D, C, A, B, E, D.
   B) D, E, A, B, C, D.
   C) D, A, B, E, C, D.
   D) D, B, E, C, A, D.
   E) None of the above

(I) 27. The cheapest link algorithm applied to the graph yields the following solution:

   A) D, C, A, B, E, D.
   B) D, E, A, B, C, D.
   C) D, A, B, E, C, D.
   D) D, B, E, C, A, D.
   E) None of the above

(II) 28. The repetitive nearest neighbor algorithm applied to the graph yields the following solution:

   A) D, C, A, B, E, D.
   B) D, E, A, B, C, D.
   C) D, A, B, E, C, D.
   D) D, B, E, C, A, D.
   E) None of the above

Questions 29 through 32 refer to the following situation: A delivery truck must deliver packages to 6 different store locations (A, B, C, D, E, and F). The trip must start and end at A. The graph below shows the distances between locations (in miles). We want to minimize the total distance traveled.

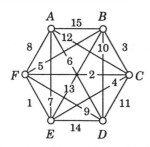

(I) 29. How many different Hamilton circuits would we have to check if we use the brute force algorithm? (Do not count the same circuit traveled backward.)

   A) 6
   B) 15
   C) 30
   D) 60
   E) None of the above

(I) 30. The nearest neighbor algorithm applied to the graph yields the following solution:

   A) A, B, C, D, E, F, A.
   B) A, C, D, B, E, F, A.
   C) A, D, F, E, C, B, A.
   D) A, E, F, C, B, D, A.
   E) None of the above

(I)   31.   The cheapest link algorithm applied to the graph yields the following solution:

A) A, B, C, D, E, F, A.
B) A, C, D, B, E, F, A.
C) A, D, F, E, C, B, A.
D) A, E, F, C, B, D, A.
E)   None of the above

(II) 32.   The repetitive nearest neighbor algorithm applied to the graph yields the following solution:

A) A, B, C, D, E, F, A.
B) A, C, D, B, E, F, A.
C) A, D, F, E, C, B, A.
D) A, E, F, C, B, D, A.
E)   None of the above

Questions 33 through 35 refer to the following situation: A delivery truck must deliver packages to 6 different store locations (A, B, C, D, E, and F). The trip must start and end at C. The graph below shows the distances between locations (in miles). We want to minimize the total distance traveled.

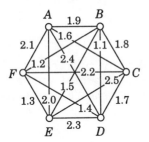

(I)   33.   The nearest neighbor algorithm applied to the graph yields the following solution:

A) C, D, E, F, A, B, C.
B) C, A, E, F, B, D, C.
C) C, B, D, F, E, A, C.
D) C, A, B, D, F, E, C.
E)   None of the above

(I)   34.   The cheapest link algorithm applied to the graph yields the following solution:

A) C, D, E, F, A, B, C.
B) C, A, E, F, B, D, C.
C) C, B, D, F, E, A, C.
D) C, A, B, D, F, E, C.
E)   None of the above

(II) 35.   The repetitive nearest neighbor algorithm applied to the graph yields the following solution:

A) C, D, E, F, A, B, C.
B) C, A, E, F, B, D, C.
C) C, B, D, F, E, A, C.
D) C, A, B, D, F, E, C.
E)   None of the above

Questions 36 through 39 refer to the following situation: A traveling salesman's territory consists of the 5 cities shown on the following mileage chart. The salesman must organize a round trip that starts and ends at Louisville (his hometown) and will pass through each of the other four cities exactly once.

	Boston	Buffalo	Chicago	Columbus	Louisville
Boston	*	446	963	735	941
Buffalo	446	*	522	326	532
Chicago	963	522	*	308	292
Columbus	735	326	308	*	209
Louisville	941	532	292	209	*

(II)   36.   The nearest neighbor algorithm applied to this problem yields the following solution:

A)   Louisville, Boston, Buffalo, Chicago, Columbus, Louisville.
B)   Louisville, Columbus, Buffalo, Boston, Chicago, Louisville.
C)   Louisville, Chicago, Buffalo, Boston, Columbus, Louisville.
D)   Louisville, Columbus, Chicago, Buffalo, Boston, Louisville.
E)   None of the above

(II)   37.   The cheapest link algorithm applied to this problem yields the following solution:

A)   Louisville, Boston, Buffalo, Chicago, Columbus, Louisville.
B)   Louisville, Columbus, Buffalo, Boston, Chicago, Louisville.
C)   Louisville, Chicago, Buffalo, Boston, Columbus, Louisville.
D)   Louisville, Columbus, Chicago, Buffalo, Boston, Louisville.
E)   None of the above

(II)   38.   The repetitive nearest neighbor algorithm applied to this problem yields the following solution:

A)   Louisville, Boston, Buffalo, Chicago, Columbus, Louisville.
B)   Louisville, Columbus, Buffalo, Boston, Chicago, Louisville.
C)   Louisville, Chicago, Buffalo, Boston, Columbus, Louisville.
D)   Louisville, Columbus, Chicago, Buffalo, Boston, Louisville.
E)   None of the above

(III)   39.   At an average cost of 25 cents per mile, the cheapest possible trip that starts at Louisville and passes through each of the other cities exactly once would cost

A) $541.75.
B) $551.00.
C) $578.25.
D) $606.50.
E)   None of the above

Questions 40 and 41 refer to the following situation: A traveling saleswoman's territory consists of the 6 cities shown on the following mileage chart. The saleswoman must organize a round trip that starts and ends at Memphis (her hometown) and will pass through each of the other five cities exactly once.

	Atlanta	Dallas	Denver	Houston	Kansas City	Memphis
Atlanta	*	795	1398	789	798	371
Dallas	795	*	781	243	489	452
Denver	1398	781	*	1019	600	1040
Houston	789	243	1019	*	710	561
Kansas City	798	489	600	710	*	451
Memphis	371	452	1040	561	451	*

(II)   40.   The nearest neighbor algorithm applied to this problem yields the following solution:

A)   Memphis, Atlanta, Denver, Kansas City, Houston, Dallas, Memphis.
B)   Memphis, Atlanta, Denver, Houston, Dallas, Kansas City, Memphis.
C)   Memphis, Dallas, Houston, Denver, Atlanta, Kansas City, Memphis.
D)   Memphis, Atlanta, Houston, Dallas, Kansas City, Denver, Memphis.
E)   None of the above

(II)   41.   The cheapest link algorithm applied to this problem yields the following solution:

A)   Memphis, Atlanta, Denver, Kansas City, Houston, Dallas, Memphis.
B)   Memphis, Atlanta, Denver, Houston, Dallas, Kansas City, Memphis.
C)   Memphis, Dallas, Houston, Denver, Atlanta, Kansas City, Memphis.
D)   Memphis, Atlanta, Houston, Dallas, Kansas City, Denver, Memphis.
E)   None of the above

Questions 42 through 44 refer to the following situation: A hypothetical management science problem requires us to find the cheapest "supercircuit" in a graph. Three algorithms are available: Algorithm 1; Algorithm 2; and Algorithm 3.

(II)   42.   Algorithm 1 always produces the cheapest supercircuit. The amount of time it takes to carry out Algorithm 1 doubles every time we increase the number of vertices by one. Algorithm 1 is

A)   an optimal and efficient algorithm.
B)   an optimal and inefficient algorithm.
C)   an approximate and efficient algorithm.
D)   an approximate and inefficient algorithm.
E)   None of the above

(II)   43.   Algorithm 2 sometimes produces the cheapest supercircuit but most of the time it
               produces a supercircuit that is only close to being the cheapest. The amount of time
               it takes to carry out Algorithm 2 is: 1 second for a graph with 1 vertex, 2 seconds for
               a graph with 2 vertices, ... 5 seconds for a graph with 5 vertices, etc. Algorithm 2 is

      A)   an optimal and efficient algorithm.
      B)   an optimal and inefficient algorithm.
      C)   an approximate and efficient algorithm.
      D)   an approximate and inefficient algorithm.
      E)   None of the above

(II)   44.   Algorithm 3 never produces a supercircuit that is off by more than 10% from the
               cheapest supercircuit. The amount of time that it takes to carry out Algorithm 3 is:
               1 second for a graph with 5 or less vertices; 30 seconds for a graph with 6 vertices;
               40 seconds for a graph with 7 vertices, and so on, increasing by 10 seconds every time
               we add a vertex (from 7 vertices on). Algorithm 3 is

      A)   an optimal and efficient algorithm.
      B)   an optimal and inefficient algorithm.
      C)   an approximate and efficient algorithm.
      D)   an approximate and inefficient algorithm.
      E)   None of the above

(II)   45.   In a complete graph with n vertices there is a total of

      A) $n(n - 1)$ edges.
      B) $n(n + 1)$ edges.
      C) $\frac{1}{2}n(n + 1)$ edges.
      D) $\frac{1}{2}n(n - 1)$ edges.
      E)   None of the above

(I)   46.   The brute force algorithm for solving the Traveling Salesman Problem is

      A)   an optimal and efficient algorithm.
      B)   an optimal and inefficient algorithm.
      C)   an approximate and efficient algorithm.
      D)   an approximate and inefficient algorithm.
      E)   None of the above

(I)   47.   The nearest neighbor algorithm for solving the Traveling Salesman Problem is

      A)   an optimal and efficient algorithm.
      B)   an optimal and inefficient algorithm.
      C)   an approximate and efficient algorithm.
      D)   an approximate and inefficient algorithm.
      E)   None of the above

(I)   48.   The repetitive nearest neighbor algorithm for solving the Traveling Salesman
              Problem is

      A)   an optimal and efficient algorithm.
      B)   an optimal and inefficient algorithm.
      C)   an approximate and efficient algorithm.
      D)   an approximate and inefficient algorithm.
      E)   None of the above

(I)   49.   The cheapest link algorithm for solving the Traveling Salesman Problem is

      A)   an optimal and efficient algorithm.
      B)   an optimal and inefficient algorithm.
      C)   an approximate and efficient algorithm.
      D)   an approximate and inefficient algorithm.
      E)   None of the above

(II) 50. $n! =$

    A) $n + (n-1)!$

    B) $n \times (n-1)!$

    C) $n! + (n-1)!$

    D) $n! \times (n-1)!$

    E) None of the above

(II) 51. In trying to solve a certain traveling salesman problem you find a solution with a total length of 500 miles. If the length of the optimal solution is 400 miles, then the relative error of your solution is

    A) 20%.

    B) 25%.

    C) 125%.

    D) 400%.

    E) None of the above

(II) 52. In trying to solve a certain traveling salesman problem you find a solution with a total length of X miles. If the length of the optimal solution is L miles, then the relative error of your solution is

    A) $\dfrac{X-L}{L}$.

    B) $X - L$.

    C) $\dfrac{X-L}{X}$.

    D) $\dfrac{X}{L}$.

    E) None of the above

Chapter 7: The Mathematics of Networks

(I)   1.   Which of the following four graphs is a tree?

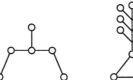

Graph 1   Graph 2   Graph 3   Graph 4

A)   Graph 1 and Graph 3
B)   Graph 2 and Graph 4
C)   Graph 2 and Graph 3
D)   Graph 1 and Graph 4
E)   None of the above

(I)   2.   A tree is

A)   any graph that has no circuits.
B)   any graph that is connected and has no circuits.
C)   any graph with one component.
D)   any graph that has no bridges.
E)   None of the above

(I)   3.   The number of edges in a tree with 57 vertices is

A)   56
B)   57
C)   58
D) 2^{57}
E)   None of the above

(I)   4.   The number of vertices in a tree with 57 edges is

A)   56
B)   57
C)   58
D) 2^{57}
E)   None of the above

(I)   5.   Graph 1 is connected and every edge is a bridge. Graph 2 is such that for any pair of vertices in the graph there is one and only one path joining them.

A)   Graph 1 must be a tree; Graph 2 must be a tree.
B)   Graph 1 must be a tree; Graph 2 may or may not be a tree.
C)   Graph 1 must be a tree; Graph 2 cannot be a tree.
D)   Graph 1 cannot be a tree; Graph 2 cannot be a tree.
E)   None of the above

(I)   6.   Suppose T is a tree with 21 vertices. Then

A) T has one bridge.
B) T can have any number of bridges.
C) T has no bridges.
D) T has 20 bridges.
E)   None of the above

(II)   7.   Suppose G graph with 39 vertices and 38 edges. Then

    A) G must be a tree.
    B) G is either a tree or it is not connected.
    C) G cannot have any circuits.
    D) G cannot have more than one path joining any two vertices.
    E)   None of the above

(II)   8.   A graph G has 42 vertices and has the property that there is one and only one path joining any two vertices of the graph. Which of the statements [A), B), C), or D)] is **not** true.

    A)   Every edge of the graph must be a bridge.
    B) G cannot have any circuits.
    C) G must be connected.
    D) G must have 41 edges.
    E)   All of the above statements are true

(I)   9.   How many spanning trees does the following graph have?

    A)   3
    B)   4
    C)   5
    D)   8
    E)   None of the above

(I)   10.   How many spanning trees does the following graph have?

    A)   3
    B)   4
    C)   5
    D)   8
    E)   None of the above

(I)   11.   How many spanning trees does the following graph have?

    A)   1
    B)   2
    C)   3
    D)   4
    E)   None of the above

(I) 12. How many spanning trees does the following graph have?

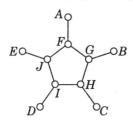

A) 4
B) 5
C) 6
D) 7
E) None of the above

(II) 13. How many spanning trees does the following graph have?

A) 15
B) 23
C) 24
D) 25
E) None of the above

(II) 14. How many different spanning trees does the following graph have?

A) 15
B) 23
C) 24
D) 25
E) None of the above

Questions 15 through 19 refer to the problem of finding the minimum spanning tree for the weighted graph shown below.

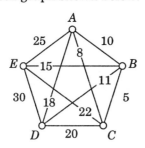

(I)   15.   Using Kruskal's algorithm which edge should we choose first?

    A)   *ED*
    B)   *EA*
    C)   *AC*
    D)   *BC*
    E)   None of the above

(I)   16.   Using Kruskal's algorithm which edge should we choose second?

    A)   *AC*
    B)   *AB*
    C)   *BD*
    D)   *CD*
    E)   None of the above

(I)   17.   Using Kruskal's algorithm which edge should we choose third?

    A)   *AC*
    B)   *AB*
    C)   *BD*
    D)   *CD*
    E)   None of the above

(I)   18.   Which of the following edges of the given graph are **not** part of the minimum spanning tree?

    A)   *AC*
    B)   *BD*
    C)   *AB*
    D)   *EB*
    E)   None of the above

(I)   19.   The total weight of the minimum spanning tree is

    A)   34.
    B)   39.
    C)   49.
    D)   60.
    E)   None of the above

Questions 20 through 24 refer to the problem of finding the minimum spanning tree for the weighted graph shown below.

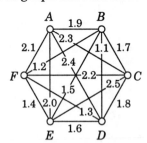

(I)   20.   Using Kruskal's algorithm which edge should we choose first?

    A)   *AB*
    B)   *AE*
    C)   *BD*
    D)   *BF*
    E)   None of the above

(I)   21.   Using Kruskal's algorithm which edge should we choose second?

    A)   *AB*
    B)   *AE*
    C)   *BD*
    D)   *BF*
    E)   None of the above

(I)   22.   Using Kruskal's algorithm which edge should we choose third?

    A)   *DF*
    B)   *EF*
    C)   *BE*
    D)   *DE*
    E)   None of the above

(I)   23.   Which of the following edges of the given graph are **not** part of the minimum spanning tree?

    A)   *AB*
    B)   *BC*
    C)   *DF*
    D)   *EF*
    E)   None of the above

(I)   24.   What is the total weight of the minimum spanning tree?

    A)   7.3
    B)   7.7
    C)   8.2
    D)   10.5
    E)   None of the above

Questions 25 through 29 refer to the problem of finding the minimum spanning tree for the weighted graph shown below.

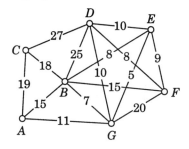

(I)   25.   Using Kruskal's algorithm which edge should we choose first?

    A)   *AB*
    B)   *BE*
    C)   *AG*
    D)   *EG*
    E)   None of the above

(I)   26.   Using Kruskal's algorithm which edge should we choose third?

    A)   *BE*
    B)   *EG*
    C)   *EF*
    D)   *DF*
    E)   None of the above

(II) 27. Using Kruskal's algorithm which edge should we choose last?

     A)   *AB*
     B)   *BC*
     C)   *AC*
     D)   *CD*
     E)   None of the above

(II) 28. Which of the following edges of the given graph are **not** part of the minimum spanning tree?

     A)   *EF*
     B)   *AC*
     C)   *AG*
     D)   *BG*
     E)   None of the above

(II) 29. The total weight of the minimum spanning tree is

     A)   36.
     B)   42.
     C)   58.
     D)   95.
     E)   None of the above

Questions 30 through 34 refer to the following situation. New telephone lines must be installed to connect 9 cities (A, B, C, D, E, F, G, H and J). Due to government regulations, the only possible connections that are allowed are shown by the edges on the graph below. The numbers on the edges indicate the cost (in millions of dollars) of each possible connection. The telephone company wishes to connect the cities in the cheapest possible way.

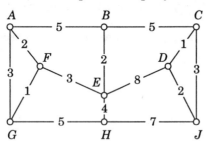

(II) 30. Using Kruskal's algorithm which edge is chosen second to last?

     A)   *AB*
     B)   *BC*
     C)   *DE*
     D)   *EH*
     E)   None of the above

(II) 31. Using Kruskal's algorithm which edge is chosen last?

     A)   *AB*
     B)   *BC*
     C)   *DE*
     D)   *EH*
     E)   None of the above

(I)   32.   In an optimal solution to this problem there will **not** be a direct connection between

     A) C and J.
     B) B and C.
     C) E and F.
     D) E and H.
     E)   All of the above will be directly connected.

(II)   33.   The total cost of the optimal solution to this problem is

     A)   18 million.
     B)   19 million.
     C)   20 million.
     D)   21 million.
     E)   None of the above

(II)   34.   The number of bridges in the optimal solution to this problem is

     A)   0.
     B)   8.
     C)   9.
     D)   10.
     E)   None of the above

(I)   35.   Which of the following statements is true about Kruskal's algorithm.

     A)   It is an efficient algorithm and it always gives the minimum spanning tree.
     B)   It is an efficient algorithm but it doesn't always give the minimum spanning tree.
     C)   It is an inefficient algorithm but it always gives the minimum spanning tree.
     D)   It is an inefficient algorithm and it never gives the minimum spanning tree.
     E)   None of the above

(II)   36.   The shortest network connecting a set of points

     A)   is always a minimum spanning tree.
     B)   is always shorter than a minimum spanning tree.
     C)   is always a Steiner tree.
     D)   is either a Steiner tree or a minimum spanning tree.
     E)   None of the above

(II)   37.   What is the length of the shortest network connecting the points A, B, and C shown in the following map?

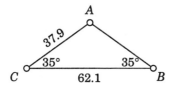

     A)   100
     B)   75.8
     C)   137.9
     D)   107.9
     E)   None of the above

(II) 38.   What is the length of the shortest network connecting the points A, B, and C shown in the following map?

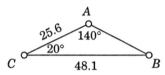

A)   51.2
B)   73.7
C)   124.9
D)   45.6
E)   None of the above

(II) 39.   The shortest network connecting the points A, B, and C shown below has

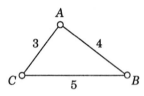

A)   a Steiner junction point outside the triangle ABC.
B)   a Steiner junction point inside the triangle ABC.
C)   a junction point at A.
D)   no junction point.
E)   None of the above

(III) 40.   The shortest network connecting the points A, B, and C shown below has

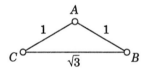

A)   a Steiner junction point outside the triangle ABC.
B)   a Steiner junction point inside the triangle ABC.
C)   a junction point at A.
D)   no junction point.
E)   None of the above

Questions 41 and 42 refer to four cities (A, B, C, and D) located at the corners of a 100 mile by 100 mile square which are to be connected by a network of power lines.

(I) 41.   Which of the following figures represents the shortest network of power lines connecting these four cities?

A) 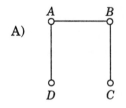   B)   C) 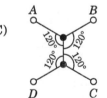   D)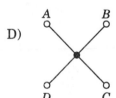

E)   None of the above

(III)   42.   At a cost of \$10,000 per mile, the cost of laying the optimal network of power lines is closest to

     A)   3 million dollars.
     B)   2.73 million dollars.
     C)   2 million dollars.
     D)   1.73 million dollars.
     E)   1 million dollars.

Questions 43 and 44 refer to four cities (A, B, C, and D) located at the corners of a 75 mile by 100 mile rectangle which are to be connected by a network of power lines.

(II)   43.   Which of the following figures represents the shortest network of power lines connecting these four cities?

A) 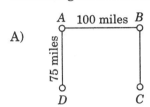   B)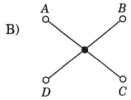

C) 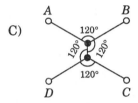   D)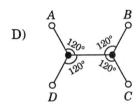

     E)   None of the above

(III)   44.   At a cost of \$10,000 per mile, the cost of laying the optimal network of power lines is closest to

     A)   3 million dollars.
     B)   2.3 million dollars.
     C)   2 million dollars.
     D)   1.7 million dollars.
     E)   1 million dollars.

(II)   45.   The number of Steiner points in a shortest network connecting three cities can only be

     A)   0.
     B)   1.
     C)   either 0 or 1.
     D)   either 0, 1, or 2.
     E)   None of the above

(II)   46.   The number of Steiner points in a shortest network connecting four cities can only be

     A)   1.
     B)   2.
     C)   either 1 or 2.
     D)   either 0, 1, or 2.
     E)   None of the above

Chapter 8: The Mathematics of Scheduling

Questions 1 through 7 refer to the following digraph.

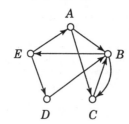

(I)   1.   Vertex A has

A)   indegree 2, outdegree 1.
B)   indegree 1, outdegree 2.
C)   indegree 0, outdegree 3.
D)   indegree 3, outdegree 0.
E)   None of the above

(I)   2.   Vertex D is

A)   incident to vertices E and B.
B)   incident to vertex C only.
C)   incident to vertex E only.
D)   incident to vertex B only.
E)   None of the above

(I)   3.   Vertex D is

A)   incident from vertices E and B.
B)   incident from vertex C only.
C)   incident from vertex E only.
D)   incident from vertex B only.
E)   None of the above

(I)   4.   Which of the following is **not** a path from vertex A to vertex E in the digraph?

A) A, B, E
B) A, C, B, E
C) A, B, C, B, E
D) A, B, D, E
E)   All of the above are paths from A to E.

(I)   5.   Which of the following is **not** a cycle in the digraph?

A) A, B, E, A
B) A, C, B, E, A
C) E, D, B, E
D) B, C, B, E, D, B
E)   All of the above are cycles in the digraph.

(I)   6.   Suppose that the vertices of the digraph represent individuals and there is an arc going from vertex X to vertex Y if and only if X "likes" Y. Which of the following statements [A), B), C), or D)] is **not** true?

A) B and C like each other.
B) C and D do not like each other.
C) E likes A and D but does not like B or C.
D) E likes B but B does not like E.
E)   All of the above statements are true.

(II)   7.   Suppose that the vertices of the digraph represent basketball teams playing in a tournament and the arcs represent games already played. An arc going from vertex X to vertex Y means that team X beat team Y. (No ties are possible in basketball.) Which of the following statements [A), B), C), or D)] is **not** true?

    A) B played a total of 5 games, winning 2 and losing 3.
    B) A defeated B and C but lost to E.
    C) D and C were the only two teams that did not play each other.
    D) B and C were the only two teams that played each other twice.
    E)   All of the above statements are true.

Questions 8 through 14 refer to a graph with 5 vertices (A, B, C, D, and E) and 9 arcs. A is incident from C, D, and E; B is incident to D and E and incident from C; D is incident to C and incident from E.

(I)   8.   Vertex A has

    A)   indegree 2, outdegree 1.
    B)   indegree 1, outdegree 2.
    C)   indegree 0, outdegree 3.
    D)   indegree 3, outdegree 0.
    E)   None of the above

(I)   9.   Vertex E has

    A)   indegree 2, outdegree 1.
    B)   indegree 1, outdegree 2.
    C)   indegree 0, outdegree 3.
    D)   indegree 3, outdegree 0.
    E)   None of the above

(I)   10.   Vertex D is

    A)   incident to vertices A and C.
    B)   incident from vertex A only.
    C)   incident from vertex B only.
    D)   incident from vertex E only.
    E)   None of the above

(I)   11.   Which of the following is **not** a path from vertex B to vertex A in the digraph?

    A) B, E, A
    B) B, D, A
    C) B, C, D, A
    D) B, D, C, A
    E)   All of the above are paths from A to E.

(I)   12.   How many cycles are there in the digraph that start and end at A?

    A)   0
    B)   1
    C)   2
    D)   3
    E)   None of the above

(I)   13.   How many cycles are there in the digraph that start and end at B?

    A)   0
    B)   1
    C)   2
    D)   3
    E)   None of the above

(I)   14.   Suppose that the vertices of the digraph represent individuals and there is an arc going from vertex X to vertex Y if and only if X "likes" Y. Which of the following statements [A), B), C), or D)] is **not** true?

     A) A doesn't like $B, C, D,$ or E.
     B) A and B do not like each other.
     C) E likes A and D but does not like B or C.
     D) B likes E but E does not like B.
     E)   All of the above statements are true.

Questions 15 through 25 refer to the following project digraph. (The numbers in parentheses represent hours.)

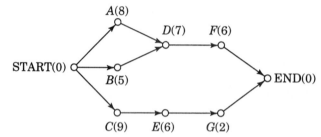

(I)   15.   The number of tasks in the project is

     A)   7.
     B)   8.
     C)   9.
     D)   10.
     E)   None of the above

(I)   16.   The number of direct precedence relations in the project is

     A)   5.
     B)   6.
     C)   8.
     D)   10.
     E)   None of the above

(I)   17.   The length of the critical path from E is

     A)   2 hours.
     B)   6 hours.
     C)   8 hours.
     D)   9 hours.
     E)   None of the above

(I)   18.   The length of the critical path from B is

     A)   5 hours.
     B)   13 hours.
     C)   18 hours.
     D)   21 hours.
     E)   None of the above

(I)   19.   The length of the critical path for the entire project is

     A)   17 hours.
     B)   18 hours.
     C)   21 hours.
     D)   26 hours.
     E)   None of the above

(II)   20.   Using the priority list C, E, G, F, B, A, D and the priority-list model to schedule this project with two processors results in a completion time of

    A)   21 hours.
    B)   22 hours.
    C)   24 hours.
    D)   26 hours.
    E)   None of the above

(II)   21.   Using the decreasing time algorithm to schedule this project with two processors results in a completion time of

    A)   21 hours.
    B)   22 hours.
    C)   24 hours.
    D)   26 hours.
    E)   None of the above

(II)   22.   Using the critical path algorithm to schedule this project with two processors results in a completion time of

    A)   21 hours.
    B)   22 hours.
    C)   24 hours.
    D)   26 hours.
    E)   None of the above

(III)   23.   The optimal completion time for this project using two processors is

    A)   20 hours.
    B)   21 hours.
    C)   22 hours.
    D)   26 hours.
    E)   None of the above

(II)   24.   Using the critical path algorithm to schedule this project with three processors results in a completion time of

    A)   20 hours.
    B)   21 hours.
    C)   22 hours.
    D)   24 hours.
    E)   None of the above

(I)   25.   Using the critical path algorithm to schedule this project with five processors results in a completion time of

    A)   20 hours.
    B)   21 hours.
    C)   22 hours.
    D)   24 hours.
    E)   None of the above

Questions 26 through 41 refer to the following project digraph. (The numbers in parentheses represent hours.)

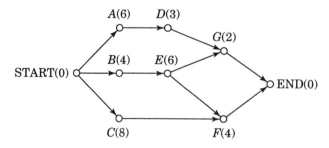

(I)   26.   What is the number of tasks in this project?

A)   6
B)   7
C)   9
D)   11
E)   None of the above

(I)   27.   What is the number of direct precedence relations in this project?

A)   6
B)   7
C)   9
D)   11
E)   None of the above

(I)   28.   The length of the critical path of this project digraph is

A)   11 hours.
B)   12 hours.
C)   14 hours.
D)   16 hours.
E)   None of the above

(II) 29.   Consider the following schedule using three processors.

Time: 0 1 2 3 4 5 6 7 8 9 10 11 12 13

P_1: A, D, Idle, G
P_2: B, E, Idle
P_3: C, F

Finishing time = 12

A)   This schedule is an optimal schedule for three processors.
B)   This schedule is not an optimal schedule because the project can be scheduled with a completion time of 11 hours.
C)   This schedule is an illegal schedule because task E was started before task C was completed.
D)   This schedule is an illegal schedule because task F was started before task E was completed.
E)   None of the above

(I)   30.   If we use the priority list F, E, A, D, B, G, C and the priority-list model to schedule this project with two processors, we should start by assigning

     A)   task A to one processor, task C to the other one.
     B)   task B to one processor, task C to the other one.
     C)   task B to one processor, task E to the other one.
     D)   task A to one processor, task B to the other one.
     E)   None of the above

(I)   31.   If we use the decreasing time algorithm to schedule this project with two processors, we should start by assigning

     A)   task A to one processor, task C to the other one.
     B)   task B to one processor, task C to the other one.
     C)   task B to one processor, task E to the other one.
     D)   task A to one processor, task B to the other one.
     E)   None of the above

(I)   32.   If we use the critical path algorithm to schedule this project with two processors, we should start by assigning

     A)   task A to one processor, task C to the other one.
     B)   task B to one processor, task C to the other one.
     C)   task B to one processor, task E to the other one.
     D)   task A to one processor, task B to the other one.
     E)   None of the above

(II)   33.   Consider the following schedule using two processors.

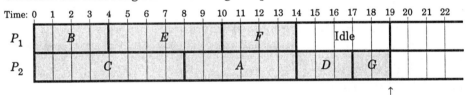

Finishing time = 19

     A)   This is the schedule one gets using the decreasing time algorithm.
     B)   This is the schedule one gets using the critical path algorithm.
     C)   This schedule is an optimal schedule.
     D)   This schedule is an illegal schedule.
     E)   None of the above

(II)   34.   Consider the following schedule using two processors.

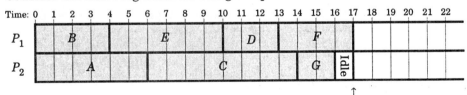

Finishing time = 17

     A)   This is the schedule one gets using the decreasing time algorithm.
     B)   This is the schedule one gets using the critical path algorithm.
     C)   This schedule is an optimal schedule.
     D)   This schedule is an illegal schedule.
     E)   None of the above

(II)   35.   If we use the priority list F, E, A, D, B, G, C and the priority-list model to schedule this project with two processors, the project completion time is

A)   18 hours.
B)   19 hours.
C)   20 hours.
D)   21 hours.
E)   None of the above

(II)   36.   Using the decreasing time algorithm to schedule the project with two processors, the project completion time is

A)   17 hours.
B)   18 hours.
C)   19 hours.
D)   20 hours.
E)   None of the above

(II)   37.   Using the decreasing time algorithm to schedule the project with two processors, the total combined idle time of the two processors is

A)   1 hour.
B)   3 hours.
C)   5 hours.
D)   7 hours.
E)   None of the above

(II)   38.   Using the critical path algorithm to schedule the project with two processors, the project completion time is

A)   17 hours.
B)   18 hours.
C)   19 hours.
D)   20 hours.
E)   None of the above

(II)   39.   Using the critical path algorithm to schedule the project with two processors, the total combined idle time of the two processors is

A)   1 hour.
B)   3 hours.
C)   5 hours.
D)   7 hours.
E)   None of the above

(II)   40.   Using the critical path algorithm to schedule the project with three processors, the project completion time is

A)   14 hours.
B)   13 hours.
C)   12 hours.
D)   11 hours.
E)   None of the above

(II)   41.   The optimal completion time for this project using six processors is

A) $5\frac{1}{2}$ hours.
B)   6 hours.
C)   14 hours.
D)   17 hours.
E)   None of the above

Questions 42 through 45 refer to the following: A project consists of 5 tasks. The lengths of the tasks (in hours) are 5, 4, 4, 3, and 3. The tasks are all independent (i.e., there are no precedence relations).

(I)   42.   Using the critical path algorithm to schedule the project with 2 processors, the completion time is

   A)   9 hours.
   B)   10 hours.
   C)   11 hours.
   D)   12 hours.
   E)   None of the above

(II)   43.   The optimal completion time of the project with 2 processors is

   A)   9 hours.
   B)   10 hours.
   C)   11 hours.
   D)   12 hours.
   E)   None of the above

(II)   44.   The optimal completion time of the project with 3 processors is

   A)   9 hours.
   B)   7 hours.
   C)   6 hours.
   D)   5 hours.
   E)   None of the above

(II)   45.   The optimal completion time of the project with 4 processors is

   A)   9 hours.
   B)   7 hours.
   C)   6 hours.
   D)   5 hours.
   E)   None of the above

(I)   46.   The decreasing time algorithm is

   A)   an optimal and efficient algorithm.
   B)   an approximate and efficient algorithm.
   C)   an optimal and inefficient algorithm.
   D)   an approximate and inefficient algorithm.
   E)   None of the above

(I)   47.   The critical path algorithm is

   A)   an optimal and efficient algorithm.
   B)   an approximate and efficient algorithm.
   C)   an optimal and inefficient algorithm.
   D)   an approximate and inefficient algorithm.
   E)   None of the above

(I)   48.   What is the number of possible priority lists in a project with 9 tasks?

   A) $(9 \times 8) / 2$
   B) $9!$
   C) 2^9
   D)   Cannot be determined without knowing the number of processors.
   E)   None of the above

(III)   49.   A project consists of all independent tasks. If we schedule the project with three
              processors, then the critical path algorithm always gives

    A)   the optimal solution.
    B)   a solution whose error is guaranteed to be no more than 16.66% of the optimal
          solution.
    C)   a solution whose error is guaranteed to be no more than 22.22% of the optimal
          solution.
    D)   a solution whose error is guaranteed to be no more than 100% of the optimal
          solution.
    E)   None of the above

(III)   50.   A project consists of all independent tasks. If we schedule the project with six
              processors, then the critical path algorithm always gives

    A)   the optimal solution.
    B)   a solution whose error is guaranteed to be no more than 16.66% of the optimal
          solution.
    C)   a solution whose error is guaranteed to be no more than 22.22% of the optimal
          solution.
    D)   a solution whose error is guaranteed to be no more than 100% of the optimal
          solution.
    E)   None of the above

Chapter 9: Spiral Growth in Nature

In questions 1 through 10, F_N represents the Nth Fibonacci number.

(I)   1. $F_{10} =$

    A)   55
    B)   34
    C)   21
    D)   10
    E)   None of the above

(I)   2. $F_9 =$

    A)   55
    B)   34
    C)   21
    D)   10
    E)   None of the above

(I)   3.   If $F_{1000} = a$ and $F_{1001} = b$, then $F_{1002} =$

    A) $a + b$.
    B) $b - a$.
    C) $a + 2a$.
    D) $2a - b$.
    E)   None of the above

(II)   4.   If $F_{1000} = a$ and $F_{1001} = b$, then $F_{1003} =$

    A) $a + b$.
    B) $b - a$.
    C) $a + 2b$.
    D) $2a - b$.
    E)   None of the above

(II)   5.   If $F_{1000} = a$ and $F_{1001} = b$, then $F_{999} =$

    A) $a + b$.
    B) $b - a$.
    C) $a + 2a$.
    D) $2a - b$.
    E)   None of the above

(II)   6.   If $F_{1000} = a$ and $F_{1001} = b$, then $F_{998} =$

    A) $a + b$.
    B) $b - a$.
    C) $a + 2a$.
    D) $2a - b$.
    E)   None of the above

(I)   7. F_{1001} / F_{1000} rounded to three decimal places gives

    A)   0.618.
    B)   1.001.
    C)   1.414.
    D)   1.618.
    E)   None of the above

(II)   8. F_{1000} / F_{1001} rounded to three decimal places gives

A)   0.618.
B)   0.999.
C)   1.414.
D)   1.618.
E)   None of the above

(I)   9. $F_{82} - F_{80} =$

A) F_{81}
B) F_{79}
C) F_2
D)   2
E)   None of the above

(II)   10.   According to Binet's formula, $F_{12} =$

A) $\dfrac{\left(\dfrac{1+\sqrt{5}}{2}\right)^{12} - \left(\dfrac{1-\sqrt{5}}{2}\right)^{12}}{\sqrt{12}}.$

B) $\dfrac{\left(1+\sqrt{5}\right)^{12} - \left(1-\sqrt{5}\right)^{12}}{5}.$

C) $\dfrac{\left(\dfrac{1+\sqrt{5}}{2}\right)^{12} - \left(\dfrac{1-\sqrt{5}}{2}\right)^{12}}{\sqrt{5}}.$

D) $\left(\dfrac{1+\sqrt{5}}{2}\right)^{12}.$

E)   None of the above

(II)   11. $\dfrac{\left(\dfrac{1+\sqrt{5}}{2}\right)^{10} - \left(\dfrac{1-\sqrt{5}}{2}\right)^{10}}{\sqrt{5}} =$

A)   55.
B)   34.
C)   21.
D)   10.
E)   None of the above

(II)   12. $\dfrac{\left(\dfrac{1+\sqrt{5}}{2}\right)^{9} - \left(\dfrac{1-\sqrt{5}}{2}\right)^{9}}{\sqrt{5}} =$

A)   55.
B)   34.
C)   21.
D)   10.
E)   None of the above

(II)   13.   According to Binet's formula, $F_N =$

A) $\left(\dfrac{1+\sqrt{5}}{2}\right)^N$.

B) $\left(\dfrac{1+\sqrt{5}}{2}\right)^N - \left(\dfrac{1-\sqrt{5}}{2}\right)^N$.

C) $\dfrac{\left(\dfrac{1+\sqrt{5}}{2}\right)^N - \left(\dfrac{1-\sqrt{5}}{2}\right)^N}{\sqrt{5}}$.

D) $\dfrac{\left[\left(\dfrac{1+\sqrt{5}}{2}\right) - \left(\dfrac{1-\sqrt{5}}{2}\right)\right]^N}{\sqrt{5}}$

E)   None of the above

(I)   14.   Rounded to three decimal places, the two solutions of $x^2 = x + 1$ are
A)   1.618 and −1.618.
B)   1.618 and −0.618.
C)   1.618 and 0.618.
D)   1.618 and 2.236.
E)   None of the above

(II)   15.   The two solutions of the equation $x^2 = x + 1$ are
A)   1 and Φ.
B) Φ and $-\Phi$
C) Φ and Φ^2.
D) Φ and $1/\Phi$.
E)   None of the above

(II)   16.   If Φ is the golden ratio and F_N is the Nth Fibonacci number, then $\Phi^N =$
A) F_N.
B) $F_N \Phi$.
C) $F_N \Phi + F_{N-1}$.
D) $F_N \Phi - F_{N-1}$.
E)   None of the above

(II)   17. $\left(\dfrac{1+\sqrt{5}}{2}\right)^7 =$

A)   13

B) $13\left(\dfrac{1+\sqrt{5}}{2}\right) + 8$ C) $13\left(\dfrac{1+\sqrt{5}}{2}\right) - 8$

D) $13\left(\dfrac{1+\sqrt{5}}{2}\right) + 8\left(\dfrac{1-\sqrt{5}}{2}\right)$ E)   None of the above

(I) 18. A golden rectangle has shorter side of length 200 ft. Which of the following numbers most closely represents the length of the longer side of the rectangle?

    A) 161.8 ft
    B) 223.6 ft
    C) 323.6 ft
    D) 447.2 ft
    E) None of the above

(II) 19. A golden rectangle has longer side of length 100 ft. Which of the following numbers most closely represents the length of the shorter side of the rectangle?

    A) 16.18 ft
    B) 50 ft
    C) 61.8 ft
    D) 161.8 ft
    E) None of the above

Questions 20 through 24 refer to the following figures:

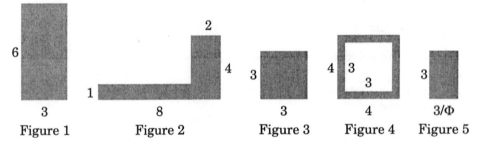

Figure 1   Figure 2   Figure 3   Figure 4   Figure 5

(I) 20. Which of the figures is a gnomon to Figure 1?

    A) Figure 2
    B) Figure 3
    C) Figure 4
    D) Figure 5
    E) None of the above

(I) 21. Which of the figures is a gnomon to Figure 2?

    A) Figure 1
    B) Figure 3
    C) Figure 4
    D) Figure 5
    E) None of the above

(I) 22. Which of the figures is a gnomon to Figure 3?

    A) Figure 1
    B) Figure 3
    C) Figure 4
    D) Figure 5
    E) None of the above

(II) 23. Which of the figures is a gnomon to Figure 5?

    A) Figure 1
    B) Figure 2
    C) Figure 3
    D) Figure 4
    E) None of the above

(II)   24.   Which of the figures is a gnomon to Figure 4?

      A)   Figure 4 does not have a gnomon.
      B)   Figure 4 is its own gnomon.
      C)   Figure 3
      D)   Figure 5
      E)   None of the above

Questions 25 and 26 refer to the circular ring with inner radius 3 and outer radius 6 shown in the figure below.

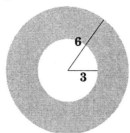

Figure 6

(I)   25.   The circular ring shown in Figure 6 is a gnomon to

      A)   another circular ring with inner radius 6 and outer radius 9.
      B)   another circular ring with inner radius 6 and outer radius 12.
      C)   a circle of radius 3.
      D)   a circle of radius 6.
      E)   None of the above

(I)   26.   A gnomon to the circular ring shown in Figure 6 is

      A)   another circular ring with inner radius 6 and outer radius 9.
      B)   another circular ring with inner radius 6 and outer radius 12.
      C)   a circle of radius 3.
      D)   a circle of radius 6.
      E)   None of the above

(II)   27.   A gnomon to an isosceles triangle with angles 72°, 72°, 36° is

      A)   another triangle with angles 72°, 72°, 36°.
      B)   a triangle with angles 36°, 36°, 108°.
      C)   an equilateral triangle.
      D)   a golden rectangle.
      E)   None of the above

(I)   28.   Rounded to three decimal places, the golden ratio F equals

      A)   0.618.
      B)   1.618.
      C)   2.618.
      D)   3.142.
      E)   None of the above

(I)   29.   The golden ratio F is the positive solution of the equation

      A) $x^2 = 1 + x.$
      B) $x^2 = 1 - x.$
      C) $x = 1 + x^2.$
      D) $x^2 = \dfrac{1}{x}.$
      E)   None of the above

(II)   30.   If A is a golden rectangle, a gnomon to A is

A)   a square of sides equal to the shorter side of A.
B)   a square of sides equal to the longer side of A.
C)   another golden rectangle whose shorter side equals the longer side of A.
D)   another golden rectangle whose longer side equals the shorter side of A.
E)   None of the above

(II)   31.   Which of the following statements is true?

A)   A 30°-60°-90° triangle is its own gnomon.
B)   An equilateral triangle is its own gnomon.
C)   An isosceles right triangle is its own gnomon.
D)   A golden rectangle is its own gnomon.
E)   None of the above

(III)   32.   Which of the following statements is true?

A)   A rectangle with dimensions $\sqrt{10}$ by $\sqrt{5}$ is its own gnomon.

B)   A rectangle with dimensions 4 by $\sqrt{2}$ is its own gnomon.

C)   A rectangle with dimensions 20 by 20Φ (where Φ is the golden ratio) is its own gnomon.

D)   A rectangle with dimensions Φ by 1/Φ (where Φ is the golden ratio) is its own gnomon.

E)   None of the above

(II)   33.   Rectangle A is 25 by 75. Rectangle B is a gnomon to rectangle A. The dimensions of rectangle B are

A)   25 by 100.
B)   25 by 150.
C)   75 by 100.
D)   75 by 200.
E)   None of the above

(II)   34.   Rectangle A is 20 by 30. Rectangle B is a gnomon to rectangle A. The dimensions of rectangle B are

A)   25 by 30.
B)   30 by 30.
C)   30 by 45.
D)   30 by 60.
E)   None of the above

(II)   35.   If the shaded "rectangular ring" is a gnomon to the white rectangle, then $x =$

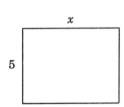 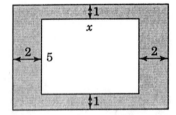

A)   6.
B)   8.
C)   10.
D)   12.
E)   None of the above

(II) 36. If the shaded figure is a gnomon to the white rectangle, then $x =$

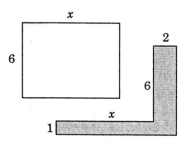

A) 6.
B) 8.
C) 10.
D) 12.
E) None of the above

(II) 37. If the rectangle below is a golden rectangle, then the approximate value of x is

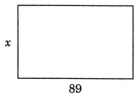

A) 34.
B) 55.
C) 89.

D) $89\left(\dfrac{1+\sqrt{5}}{2}\right).$

E) None of the above

Questions 38 and 39 refer to the sequence A_N defined by $A_1 = 5$, $A_2 = 5$, $A_N = A_{N-1} + A_{N-2}$.

(II) 38. The relation between A_N and F_N is given by

A) $A_N = F_N.$
B) $A_N = F_N + 4.$
C) $A_N = F_{N+4}.$
D) $A_N = 5F_N.$
E) None of the above

(II) 39. As the values of N get large, the ratios A_{N+1} / A_N approach

A) $\Phi.$
B) $5\Phi.$
C) $25\Phi.$
D) $\Phi + 5.$
E) None of the above

(II) 40. Which of the following statements [A), B), C), or D)] is **not** true?

A) There are figures that have more than one gnomon.
B) There are figures that have no gnomons.
C) There are figures that are gnomons to themselves.
D) If G is a gnomon to A, then A must be a gnomon to G.
E) All of the above statements are true.

Chapter 10: The Mathematics of Population Growth

Questions 1 through 6 refer to the following example: The number of cars sold weekly by a new automobile dealership grows according to a linear growth model. The first week the dealership sold 2 cars ($P_1 = 2$). The second week the dealership sold 6 cars ($P_2 = 6$).

(I)　1.　How many cars were sold in the third week?

　　　　A)　24
　　　　B)　18
　　　　C)　12
　　　　D)　10
　　　　E)　None of the above

(I)　2.　How many cars were sold in the 51st week?

　　　　A)　206
　　　　B)　202
　　　　C)　106
　　　　D)　104
　　　　E)　None of the above

(II)　3.　If the manager gets a $100 bonus for every car sold, how much total bonus money did the manager make in the first four weeks?

　　　　A)　$8000
　　　　B)　$5600
　　　　C)　$3200
　　　　D)　$1400
　　　　E)　None of the above

(I)　4.　If P_N denotes the number of cars sold in the Nth week then

　　　　A)　$P_N = P_{N-1} + 4$
　　　　B)　$P_N = P_{N-1} + 2$
　　　　C)　$P_N = 4P_{N-1}$
　　　　D)　$P_N = P_{N-1} - 4$
　　　　E)　None of the above

(II)　5.　If P_N denotes the number of cars sold in the Nth week then

　　　　A)　$P_N = 4N + 2$
　　　　B)　$P_N = 4N - 2$
　　　　C)　$P_N = 2N + 4$
　　　　D)　$P_N = N^2 + N$
　　　　E)　None of the above

(II)　6.　In the first 50 weeks the dealership sold a total of

　　　　A)　2000 cars.
　　　　B)　4996 cars.
　　　　C)　5000 cars.
　　　　D)　5004 cars.
　　　　E)　None of the above

(I)   7. $\underbrace{5 + 8 + 11 + 14 + \ldots + 299 + 302}_{100 \text{ terms}} =$

A)   30,700
B)   30,200
C)   15,350
D)   15,100
E)   None of the above

(II)   8. $\underbrace{7 + 2 - 3 - 8 - \ldots - 483 - 488}_{100 \text{ terms}} =$

A)   −973
B)   −24,050
C)   −24,750
D)   24,750
E)   None of the above

(II)   9. $\underbrace{5 + 8 + 11 + 14 + \ldots}_{321 \text{ terms}} =$

A)   154,400
B)   155,685
C)   308,800
D)   311,370
E)   None of the above

(II)   10. $\underbrace{2 + 12 + 22 + 32 + \ldots}_{151 \text{ terms}} =$

A)   113,552
B)   113,401
C)   114,156
D)   114,307
E)   None of the above

(II)   11. $5 + 8 + 11 + \ldots + 755 =$

A) $\dfrac{760 \text{ ¥ } 251}{2}$

B) $\dfrac{760 \text{ ¥ } 250}{2}$

C) $\dfrac{760 \text{ ¥ } 750}{2}$

D) $\dfrac{760 \text{ ¥ } 747}{2}$

E)   None of the above

(II)   12. $7 + 10 + 13 + \ldots + 172 =$

A) $\dfrac{179 \text{ ¥ } 55}{2}$

B) $\dfrac{179 \text{ ¥ } 56}{2}$

C) $\dfrac{179 \text{ ¥ } 165}{2}$

D) $\dfrac{172 \text{ ¥ } 7}{2}$

E)   None of the above

(I)   13.   In an arithmetic sequence with first term P_1 and common difference d, the Nth term is given by

    A) $d + (N-1)P_1$.
    B) $d + NP_1$.
    C) $P_1 + Nd$.
    D) $P_1 + (N-1)d$.
    E)   None of the above

(III) 14.   In an arithmetic sequence with first term P_1 and common difference d, the sum of the first 200 terms is given by

    A) $100(2P_1 + 200d)$.
    B) $200(2P_1 + 199d)$.
    C) $100(2P_1 + 199d)$.
    D) $200(2P_1 + 200d)$.
    E)   None of the above

(I)   15.   In an geometric sequence with first term P_1 and common ratio r, the 100th term of the sequence is given by

    A) $P_1 + r^{99}$.
    B) $P_1 \times r^{99}$.
    C) $P_1 \times r^{100}$.
    D) $P_1 + r^{100}$.
    E)   None of the above

(I)   16.   A bank offers a 6% annual interest rate compounded monthly. The periodic interest is

    A)   0.5.
    B)   0.06.
    C)   0.05.
    D)   0.005.
    E)   None of the above

(II) 17.   A bank offers a 6% annual interest rate compounded monthly. The annual yield is approximately

    A)   6.17%.
    B)   6%.
    C)   5.75%.
    D)   6.27%.
    E)   None of the above

(I)   18.   A bank offers a 7.3% annual interest rate compounded daily. The periodic interest is

    A)   0.00068.
    B)   0.00073.
    C)   0.0002.
    D)   0.00002.
    E)   None of the above

(II)   19.   A bank offers a 7.3% annual interest rate compounded daily. The annual yield is approximately

     A)   13.23%·
     B)   10.72%·
     C)   8.03%·
     D)   7.57%·
     E)   None of the above

(I)   20.   How much does $543 grow to in four years if left in a savings account that pays 10.5% interest compounded annually?

     A) $543(10.5)^4$
     B) $543(.105)^4$
     C) $543(1.105)^4$
     D) $543(1.05)^4$
     E)   None of the above

(I)   21.   How much does $823.25 grow to in five years if left in a savings account that pays 12% annual interest compounded monthly?

     A) $823.25(1.12)^5$
     B) $823.25(1.12)^{60}$
     C) $823.25\left(\dfrac{1.12}{12}\right)^{60}$
     D) $823.25\left(1+\dfrac{.12}{12}\right)^{60}$
     E)   None of the above

(III)   22.   How much does P grow to in ten years if left in a savings account that pays $i\%$ interest compounded four times a year?

     A) $P\left(1+\dfrac{i}{4}\right)^{40}$
     B) $P\left(\dfrac{1+i}{4}\right)^{40}$
     C) $P\left(1+\dfrac{100i}{4}\right)^{40}$
     D) $P\left(1+\dfrac{i}{400}\right)^{40}$
     E)   None of the above

(II)   23.   On January 1 you invest $300 for one year and leave all interest to accumulate. On April 1, $5 is credited to your account; on July 1, $10 is credited to your account; on October 1, $15 is credited to your account; on December 30, $10 is credited to your account. What is the annual yield on your investment?

     A)   10%
     B)   12.5%
     C)   approximately 13.3%
     D)   cannot be determined from this information
     E)   None of the above

(III) 24. Monthly payments on a $100,000 loan at 12% annual interest amortized over 100 years will be close to

A) $1200.
B) $1000.
C) $833.33.
D) $333.33.
E) None of the above

(II) 25. $1 + 5 + 5^2 + 5^3 + \ldots + 5^{207} =$

A) 5^{208}
B) $\dfrac{5^{206} - 1}{4}$
C) $\dfrac{5^{208}}{4} - 1$
D) $\dfrac{5^{208} - 1}{4}$
E) None of the above

(II) 26. $5 + 5 \times 3 + 5 \times 3^2 + 5 \times 3^3 + \cdots + 5 \times 3^{78} =$

A) $5 \times (3^{79} - 1)$
B) $2.5 \times (3^{79} - 1)$
C) $2.5 \times (3^{78} - 1)$
D) $5 \times (3^{78} - 1)$
E) None of the above

Questions 27 and 28 refer to a certain population of fish in a pond whose growth is described by the logistic equation. The growth parameter for this type of fish is $r = 3.0$.

(I) 27. If the starting population is given by $p_1 = 0.2$, then after one breeding season the population of the pond is given by

A) $p_2 = 0.16$.
B) $p_2 = 0.42$.
C) $p_2 = 0.48$.
D) $p_2 = 0.6$.
E) None of the above

(II) 28. If originally the pond is stocked to 50% of its carrying capacity, then the population of the pond after the second breeding season is

A) 75% of the pond's carrying capacity.
B) 56.25% of the pond's carrying capacity.
C) 50% of the pond's carrying capacity.
D) 25% of the pond's carrying capacity.
E) None of the above

(III) 29. Suppose that we have a confined colony of squirrels growing according to the logistic growth model. Suppose that the growth parameter for this type of squirrel is $r = \dfrac{29}{10}$. Suppose also that the starting population is $p_1 = \dfrac{20}{29}$ Then $p_3 =$

A) $\dfrac{18}{29}$.
B) $\dfrac{10}{29}$.
C) $\dfrac{99}{145}$.
D) $\dfrac{107}{145}$.
E) None of the above

(II)   30.   Suppose that in a population growing according to the logistic growth model we have $p_5 = \frac{10}{28}$ and $p_6 = \frac{20}{28}$. Then $r =$

A) $\frac{28}{9}$.

B) $\frac{28}{10}$.

C) $\frac{10}{28}$.

D)   2.

E)   None of the above

Chapter 11: Symmetry

Questions 1 through 8 refer to the square $ABCD$ with center O as shown below. ($M, N, P,$ and Q are the midpoints of the sides.)

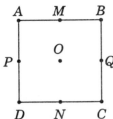

(I)   1.   Which of the following reflections is **not** a symmetry of the square?

    A)   the reflection with axis the line passing through A and C
    B)   the reflection with axis the line passing through A and B
    C)   the reflection with axis the line passing through M and N
    D)   the reflection with axis the line passing through P and Q
    E)   All of the above are symmetries of the square.

(I)   2.   Which of the following rotations is a symmetry of the square?

    A)   a 90° clockwise rotation with center A
    B)   a 90° clockwise rotation with center P
    C)   a 90° clockwise rotation with center O
    D)   a 60° clockwise rotation with center O
    E)   None of the above

(I)   3.   Which of the following translations is a symmetry of the square?

    A)   a translation that sends A to B
    B)   a translation that sends A to C
    C)   a translation that sends A to O
    D)   a translation that sends P to Q
    E)   None of the above

(I)   4.   The image of A under the reflection with axis the line passing through M and P is

    A) B.
    B) C.
    C) D.
    D) O.
    E)   None of the above

(I)   5.   The image of A under a 90° clockwise rotation with center O is

    A) B.
    B) C.
    C) D.
    D) M.
    E)   None of the above

(I)   6.   A translation sends the point A to the point Q. The image of P under this translation is

    A) C.
    B) N.
    C) B.
    D) O.
    E)   None of the above

(II)   7.   A glide reflection sends the point A to the point Q and the point P to the point C. The image of B under this glide reflection is

    A) A.
    B) P.
    C) D.
    D) N.
    E)   None of the above

(II)   8.   A glide reflection sends the point A to the point Q and the point P to the point C. The axis of this glide reflection is a line passing through the points

    A) A and B.
    B) P and Q.
    C) A and Q.
    D) M and N.
    E)   None of the above

(I)   9.   What are the symmetries of the letter C?

    A)   a 90° rotation
    B)   a reflection with axis a vertical line
    C)   a reflection with axis a horizontal line
    D)   the letter C has no symmetries
    E)   None of the above

(II)   10.   The letter C has symmetry type

    A) Z_1.
    B) D_1.
    C) Z_2.
    D) D_2.
    E)   None of the above

(I)   11.   What are the symmetries of the letter D?

    A)   a 90° rotation
    B)   a reflection with axis a vertical line
    C)   a reflection with axis a horizontal line
    D)   the letter D has no symmetries
    E)   None of the above

(I)   12.   Which of the following are symmetries of the letter Z?

    A)   a reflection with axis a vertical line
    B)   a reflection with axis a horizontal line
    C)   a reflection with axis a diagonal line
    D)   a 180° rotation
    E)   None of the above

(II)   13.   The letter Q has symmetry type

    A) Z_1.
    B) D_1.
    C) Z_2.
    D) D_2.
    E)   None of the above

(II)   14.   The letter Z has symmetry type

   A) Z_1.
   B) D_1.
   C) Z_2.
   D) D_2.
   E)   None of the above

(II)   15.   The symmetry type of an isosceles, nonequilateral triangle is

   A) Z_2.
   B) D_1.
   C) Z_3.
   D) D_2.
   E)   None of the above

(I)   16.   Which of the following letters has the same symmetry type as the letter H?

   A)   W
   B)   E
   C)   I
   D)   D
   E)   None of the above

(I)   17.   If an object has a 60° clockwise rotation as one of its symmetries then it must also have as a symmetry

   A)   a 90° clockwise rotation.
   B)   a 180° rotation.
   C)   a reflection.
   D)   a translation.
   E)   None of the above

(I)   18.   If an object has a 120° clockwise rotation as one of its symmetries then it must also have as a symmetry

   A)   a 60° clockwise rotation.
   B)   a 60° counterclockwise rotation.
   C)   a 120° counterclockwise rotation.
   D)   a 180° rotation.
   E)   None of the above

(I)   19.   The result of applying a 50° clockwise rotation followed by a 50° counterclockwise rotation with the same center is

   A)   a 100° clockwise rotation.
   B)   a 100° counterclockwise rotation.
   C)   the identity motion.
   D)   a reflection.
   E)   None of the above

(II)   20.   The result of applying two consecutive reflections with parallel axes is equivalent to a single

   A)   translation.
   B)   reflection.
   C)   rotation.
   D)   glide reflection.
   E)   None of the above

(II)   21.   The result of applying the same glide reflection twice is equivalent to a single

    A)   glide reflection.
    B)   translation.
    C)   rotation.
    D)   reflection.
    E)   None of the above

(II)   22.   The result of applying a translation followed by a rotation is equivalent to a single

    A)   reflection.
    B)   translation or rotation.
    C)   glide reflection.
    D)   translation.
    E)   None of the above

(I)   23.   Of the four basic rigid motions, which are the improper rigid motions?

    A)   reflections only
    B)   reflections and glide reflections only
    C)   translations and rotations only
    D)   reflections, rotations, translations, and glide reflections
    E)   None of the above

(I)   24.   Of the four basic rigid motions, which are the proper rigid motions?

    A)   reflections only
    B)   reflections and glide reflections only
    C)   translations and rotations only
    D)   reflections, rotations, translations, and glide reflections
    E)   None of the above

(I)   25.   Which of the four basic rigid motions must always be a symmetry of an infinite pattern?

    A)   a reflection
    B)   a rotation
    C)   a translation
    D)   a glide reflection
    E)   None of the above

(II)   26.   The complete symmetries of the pattern ... Z Z Z Z Z Z ... are

    A)   translations and horizontal reflections only .
    B)   translation and vertical reflections only .
    C)   translations and 45° rotations only.
    D)   translations and 180° rotations only.
    E)   None of the above

(II)   27.   The complete symmetries of the pattern ... p b q d p b q d p b q d ... are

    A)   translations only.
    B)   translations and glide reflections only.
    C)   translations and 180° rotations only.
    D   translations, glide reflections, and 180° rotations only.
    E)   None of the above

(II)   28.   The complete symmetries of the pattern ... p b p b p b ... are

    A)   translations only.
    B)   translations and glide reflections only.
    C)   translations and 180° rotations only.
    D   translations, glide reflections, and 180° rotations only.
    E)   None of the above

(II) 29. Which of the following statements [A), B), C), or D)] is **not** true about border patterns?

A) There are only seven different types of such patterns.
B) Every border pattern must have a translation as one of its symmetries.
C) Every border pattern must have a reflection as one of its symmetries.
D) There is a border pattern whose only symmetry is a horizontal translation.
E) None of the above

(I) 30. In a border pattern, the only possible angle(s) of rotational symmetry are

A) 180°.
B) 90°, 180°.
C) 60°, 90°, 180°.
D) 60°, 90°, 120°, 180°.
E) None of the above

(II) 31. In a wallpaper pattern,

A) there may or may not be translation symmetry.
B) there is translation symmetry in exactly one direction.
C) there is translation symmetry in at least two different directions.
D) there is translation symmetry in at least four different directions.
E) None of the above

(II) 32. In a wallpaper pattern, the only possible angle(s) of rotational symmetry are

A) 180°.
B) 90°, 180°.
C) 60°, 90°, 180°.
D) 60°, 90°, 120°, 180°.
E) None of the above

(II) 33. The complete symmetries of the wallpaper pattern

$$\vdots$$

T T T T T T T

··· T T T T T T T ···

T T T T T T

$$\vdots$$

are the identity and

A) translations only.
B) translations and horizontal reflections only.
C) translations and vertical reflections only.
D) translations and 180° rotations only.
E) None of the above

(II)   34.   The complete symmetries of the wallpaper pattern

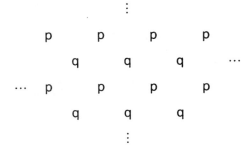

are the identity and

A)   translations only.
B)   translations and glide reflections only.
C)   translations and vertical reflections only.
D)   translations, reflection and rotations only.
E)   None of the above

(I)   35.   The identity motion is

A)   a symmetry of every object.
B)   a symmetry of finite objects only.
C)   a symmetry of borders and wallpapers only.
D)   not a symmetry.
E)   None of the above

(III)   36.   Which of the following statements [A), B), C), or D)] is **not** true?

A)   There are exactly seven different types of border patterns.
B)   Every border pattern must have translation symmetry in the direction of the pattern.
C)   There are seventeen different types of wallpaper patterns.
D)   Every wallpaper pattern must have translation symmetries in at least two different directions.
E)   All of the above statements are true.

Chapter 12: Fractal Geometry

Questions 1 through 9 refer to the figures and recursive rules given below.

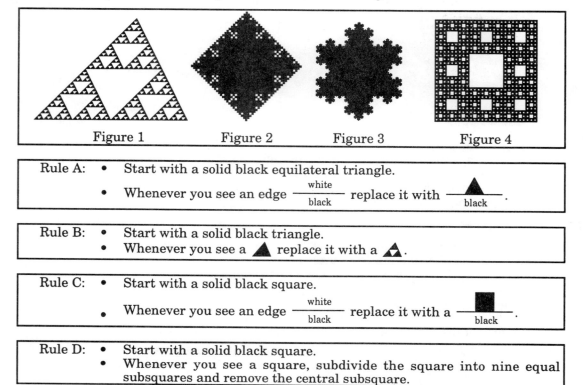

Figure 1   Figure 2   Figure 3   Figure 4

Rule A: •   Start with a solid black equilateral triangle.
      •   Whenever you see an edge $\frac{white}{black}$ replace it with ▲ .

Rule B: •   Start with a solid black triangle.
      •   Whenever you see a ▲ replace it with a ◭ .

Rule C: •   Start with a solid black square.
      •   Whenever you see an edge $\frac{white}{black}$ replace it with a ⬛ .

Rule D: •   Start with a solid black square.
      •   Whenever you see a square, subdivide the square into nine equal subsquares and remove the central subsquare.

Rule E: •   Start with a solid black equilateral triangle.
      •   Whenever you see an edge $\frac{white}{black}$ replace it with $black\sqrt{}black$.

(I)   1.   Which of the figures approximates the result of recursively applying Rule A infinitely many times?

     A)   Figure 1
     B)   Figure 2
     C)   Figure 3
     D)   Figure 4
     E)   None of the above

(I)   2.   Which of the figures approximates the result of recursively applying Rule B infinitely many times?

     A)   Figure 1
     B)   Figure 2
     C)   Figure 3
     D)   Figure 4
     E)   None of the above

(I)   3.   Which of the figures approximates the result of recursively applying Rule C infinitely
            many times?

            A)   Figure 1
            B)   Figure 2
            C)   Figure 3
            D)   Figure 4
            E)   None of the above

(I)   4.   Which of the figures approximates the result of recursively applying Rule D infinitely
            many times?

            A)   Figure 1
            B)   Figure 2
            C)   Figure 3
            D)   Figure 4
            E)   None of the above

(II)   5.   Which of the figures approximates the result of recursively applying Rule E infinitely
            many times?

            A)   Figure 1
            B)   Figure 2
            C)   Figure 3
            D)   Figure 4
            E)   None of the above

(I)   6.   Which of the figures best approximates the Koch snowflake?

            A)   Figure 1
            B)   Figure 2
            C)   Figure 3
            D)   Figure 4
            E)   None of the above

(I)   7.   Which of the figures best approximates the Sierpinski gasket?

            A)   Figure 1
            B)   Figure 2
            C)   Figure 3
            D)   Figure 4
            E)   None of the above

(I)   8.   Which of the rules, when recursively applied infinitely many times does **not** produce
            a figure with exact symmetry of scale?

            A)   Rule B
            B)   Rule C
            C)   Rule D
            D)   Rule E
            E)   All of the above produce figures with exact symmetry of scale.

(III) 9.   What is the area of the figure obtained when we recursively apply Rule E infinitely
            many times, given that the area of the starting equilateral triangle is 10?

            A)   0
            B)   4
            C)   16
            D)   infinite
            E)   None of the above

(I)   10.   If the area of the starting triangle in the construction of the Koch snowflake is 10, then the area of the Koch snowflake is

A)   0.
B)   16.
C)   20.
D)   infinite.
E)   None of the above

(I)   11.   Suppose that the perimeter of the starting triangle in the construction of the Koch snowflake is 10. Then the length of the boundary of the Koch snowflake is

A)   0.
B)   16.
C)   20.
D)   infinite.
E)   None of the above

(I)   12.   The Koch snowflake is a geometric shape with

A)   infinite area and infinite perimeter.
B)   infinite area and finite perimeter.
C)   finite area and finite perimeter.
D)   finite area and infinite perimeter.
E)   None of the above

(I)   13.   If the area of the starting triangle in the construction of the Sierpinski gasket is 10, then the area of the Sierpinski gasket is

A)   0.
B)   16.
C)   20.
D)   infinite.
E)   None of the above

Questions 14 through 19 refer to the Mandelbrot replacement process described by:
- Start: Pick a seed s and let $x = s$.
- Recursive step: If x is the number obtained in the previous step, replace x with $x^2 + s$.

(I)   14.   For the seed $s = 3$, the first two steps produce

A)   3 and 6.
B)   6 and 142.
C)   12 and 147.
D)   3 and 3.
E)   None of the above

(I)   15.   For the seed $s = -1$, the first three steps produce

A)   0, 0, and 0.
B)   2, 3, and 7.
C)   0, 1, and 0.
D)   0, -1, and 0.
E)   None of the above

(II)   16.   For the seed $s = -1$, the Mandelbrot replacement process

    A)   goes off to infinity.
    B)   is periodic.
    C)   gives values that get closer and closer to −1.
    D)   gives values that have no pattern.
    E)   None of the above

(II)   17.   For the seed $s = -3$, the Mandelbrot replacement process

    A)   goes off to infinity.
    B)   is periodic.
    C)   gives values that get closer and closer to −1.
    D)   gives values that have no pattern.
    E)   None of the above

(II)   18.   Suppose that when we apply the Mandelbrot replacement process we get Step 6: $x = 2$, and Step 7: $x = 2$. Then the seed is

    A) $s = 1$.
    B) $s = -1$.
    C) $s = -2$.
    D) $s = 2$.
    E)   None of the above

(III)   19.   Suppose that we apply the Mandelbrot replacement process with seed $s = \sqrt{2}$. Then in Step 2 we get

    A) $6 + 5\sqrt{2}$.
    B) $6 + \sqrt{2}$.
    C) $4 + \sqrt{2}$.
    D) $2 + 2\sqrt{2}$.
    E)   None of the above

(II)   20.   Of the following objects in nature, which one could never have symmetry of scale?

    A)   a cloud
    B)   a mountain
    C)   a coastline
    D)   a soap bubble
    E)   All of the above could have symmetry of scale.

(II)   21.   Which of the following geometric objects has exact symmetry of scale?

    A)   a circle
    B)   a triangle
    C)   a sphere
    D)   the Mandelbrot set
    E)   None of the above

(I)   22.   Which of the following objects has exact symmetry of scale?

    A)   the Koch snowflake
    B)   the Mandelbrot set
    C)   a tree
    D)   a head of cauliflower
    E)   None of the above

(I)   23.   Which of the following objects is **not** a fractal?

    A)   the Mandelbrot set
    B)   the Sierpinski gasket
    C)   the Koch curve
    D)   the Statue of Liberty
    E)   None of the above

(I)   24.   Which of the following objects has approximate symmetry of scale but not exact symmetry of scale?

    A)   the Mandelbrot set
    B)   the Sierpinski gasket
    C)   the Koch curve
    D)   the Statue of Liberty
    E)   None of the above

(I)   25.   If $a = 1 + i$, and $b = i$ then $ab =$

    A) $-1 + i$.
    B) $1 + i$.
    C) 0.
    D) 2.
    E)   None of the above

(II) 26.   If $a = 1 + i$ then $a^2 + a =$

    A) $3 + 3i$.
    B) $1 + 3i$.
    C) $2 + 4i$.
    D) $3i$.
    E)   None of the above

(II) 27.   If we apply the Mandelbrot replacement process to the seed $s = i$, the first step produces

    A) -1.
    B) $-i$.
    C) $-1 + i$.
    D) $2i$.
    E)   None of the above

(III) 28.   If we apply the Mandelbrot replacement process to the seed $s = 1 + i$, the second step produces

    A) $-1 - i$.
    B) $1 + 3i$.
    C) $3 - 3i$.
    D) $-7 + 7i$.
    E)   None of the above

(II) 29.   Suppose that at a certain step, the Mandelbrot replacement process produces the value $x = 5$ and at the next step it produces the value $x = 26$. Then the seed s equals

    A) 21.
    B) 2.
    C) $\sqrt{2}$.
    D) 1.
    E)   None of the above

(III)   30.   Suppose that when we apply the Mandelbrot replacement process we get: Step 8: $x = a$; Step 9: $x = b$; Step 10: $x = -a$. Which of the following is the value of x in Step 11?

   A) $x = b$
   B) $x = -b$
   C) $x = a^2 + b$
   D) $x = a^2$
   E)   None of the above

Chapter 13: Collecting Statistical Data

Questions 1 through 8 refer to the following: As a part of a statistics project, a 6th grade teacher brings to class a container with 300 red marbles and 1200 white marbles which are thoroughly mixed. To figure out how many red marbles are in the container without actually counting them all, a student randomly draws 250 marbles from the container. Of the 250 marbles drawn, 53 are red.

(I)   1.   The data collection method in this example can best be described as

    A)   a census.
    B)   a survey.
    C)   a clinical study.
    D)   a controlled study.
    E)   None of the above

(I)   2.   The population consists of

    A)   the 1500 marbles in the container.
    B)   the 300 red marbles in the container.
    C)   the 250 marbles drawn by the student.
    D)   the 53 red marbles drawn by the student.
    E)   None of the above

(I)   3.   The N-value for this population is

    A)   53.
    B)   250.
    C)   300.
    D)   1500.
    E)   None of the above

(I)   4.   The sample consists of

    A)   the 1500 marbles in the container.
    B)   the 300 red marbles in the container.
    C)   the 250 marbles drawn by the student.
    D)   the 53 red marbles drawn by the student.
    E)   None of the above

(I)   5.   The sampling rate is

    A) $16\frac{2}{3}\%$.
    B) $12\frac{1}{2}\%$.
    C)   30%.
    D)   75%.
    E)   None of the above

(I)   6.   Suppose that the student is given the N-value. What is a reasonable estimate for the number of red marbles in the container?

    A)   203.
    B)   269.
    C)   318.
    D)   422.
    E)   None of the above

(I)   7.   The sampling error is

      A)   78%.
      B)   2%.
      C)   1.5%.
      D)   1.2%.
      E)   None of the above

(I)   8.   The sampling method used in this example is called

      A)   stratified sampling.
      B)   quota sampling.
      C)   simple random sampling.
      D)   random sampling, but not simple random sampling.
      E)   None of the above

Questions 9 through 13 refer to the following: In order to determine how American college students feel about a proposed national law that would raise the minimum drinking age to 22, a survey was conducted. 500 undergraduates students from Southern Hawaii University were interviewed. Each of the five interviewers hired to conduct the survey was told to interview 25 freshmen, 25 sophomores, 25 juniors, and 25 seniors. Of the 500 students interviewed, 15% were in favor of raising the minimum drinking age to 22, 75% were opposed, and 10% had no opinion.

(I)   9.   The population for this survey is

      A)   the 500 students that were interviewed.
      B)   the 450 students that had an opinion.
      C)   all undergraduates at Southern Hawaii University.
      D)   all American college students.
      E)   None of the above

(I)   10.   The sample for this survey is

      A)   all undergraduates at Southern Hawaii University.
      B)   all American college students.
      C)   the 500 students that were interviewed.
      D)   the 450 students that had an opinion.
      E)   None of the above

(I)   11.   Based on the fact that 15% of the students interviewed were in favor of raising the minimum drinking age to 22, the value 15% is

      A)   a statistic.
      B)   a population.
      C)   a parameter.
      D)   a sample.
      E)   None of the above

(I)   12.   The results of this survey are unreliable primarily because of

      A)   selection bias only.
      B)   non-response bias only.
      C)   both selection bias and non-response bias.
      D)   the absence of a control group.
      E)   None of the above

(I)   13.   The sampling method used for this survey is called

      A)   simple random sampling.
      B)   quota sampling.
      C)   stratified sampling.
      D)   random sampling.
      E)   None of the above

Questions 14 through 16 refer to the following example. A child has an enormous jar in which he has been saving all of his spare change. In order to determine exactly how much money he has in the jar, he dumps all the coins on the floor and counts them. Under the watchful eye of his mother he counts 254 pennies, 198 nickels, 132 dimes, and 91 quarters.

(I)   14.   The data collection method used in this example is called

         A)   a survey.
         B)   a census.
         C)   a controlled experiment.
         D)   random sampling.
         E)   None of the above

(I)   15.   In the statement "There were 91 quarters in the jar", the number 91 is

         A)   a parameter.
         B)   a statistic.
         C)   a population.
         D)   a confounding variable.
         E)   None of the above

(I)   16.   If the population in this example is defined to be all the coins in the jar, the N-value is

         A)   254.
         B)   198.
         C)   132.
         D)   91.
         E)   None of the above

Questions 17 through 20 refer to the following example. In order to determine the effects of a new pill that is supposed to reduce hair loss, a researcher conducts the following experiment: 500 volunteer subjects (300 men and 200 women) all of which suffer some degree of hair loss are selected to participate in the study. The researcher gives the women the real pill and the men a sugar pill, but only the researcher knows this.

(I)   17.   Which of the following statements [A), B), C), or D)] is **not** true?

         A)   The experiment is a clinical study.
         B)   The experiment is a controlled placebo experiment.
         C)   The experiment is a randomized controlled experiment.
         D)   The control group consists of 300 people.
         E)   All of the above statements are true.

(I)   18.   Which of the following statements is true?

         A)   The experiment is a double blind experiment.
         B)   The experiment is a blind experiment, but not a double blind experiment.
         C)   The experiment is a double blind experiment, but not a blind experiment.
         D)   The experiment is not a blind experiment.
         E)   None of the above

(I)   19.   In this experiment, which is the placebo group?

         A)   the 300 men
         B)   the 200 women
         C)   the subjects that responded to the treatment
         D)   There is no placebo group.
         E)   None of the above

(I) 20.   The results of this experiment are likely to be invalid mostly because

  A)   the subjects were volunteers.
  B)   the gender of the patient could be a confounding variable in this experiment.
  C)   the treatment group and control group were not the same size.
  D)   the subjects did not know if they were getting the real treatment.
  E)   None of the above

Questions 21 through 24 refer to the following: In order to determine the effectiveness of a new vaccine that is alleged to cure "math anxiety", an experiment was conducted. One thousand volunteer college students enrolled in math courses across the U.S. were chosen. The 1,000 students were broken up into two groups. Those enrolled in calculus courses or higher were given the real vaccine. The students in remedial and basic math courses were given a fake vaccine consisting of sugared water. None of the students knew whether they were being given the real or the fake vaccine, but the researcher conducting the experiment knew. At the end of the semester the students were given a test that measured their level of math anxiety. The students in the treatment group showed significantly lower levels of math anxiety than those in the control group. On the basis of this experiment the vaccine was advertised as being highly effective in fighting math anxiety.

(I) 21.   The control group in this experiment consists of

  A)   the 1,000 volunteer college students used for the study.
  B)   the students given the real vaccine.
  C)   the students given the fake vaccine.
  D)   This experiment has no control group because it used volunteers.
  E)   None of the above

(I) 22.   This experiment can best be described as a

  A)   double blind randomized controlled experiment.
  B)   double blind controlled placebo experiment.
  C)   blind randomized controlled experiment.
  D)   blind controlled placebo experiment.
  E)   None of the above

(I) 23.   The results of this experiment should be considered unreliable because

  A)   only college students were used.
  B)   the treatment and control groups were not the same size.
  C)   the sample was too small.
  D)   the treatment and control groups represented two very different segments of the population.
  E)   None of the above

(I) 24.   Which of the following is the most likely confounding variable for this experiment?

  A)   the student's background in mathematics
  B)   the student's grade level (freshman, sophomore, junior, senior)
  C)   the type of college attended (two year, four year, university)
  D)   the student's sex (male, female)
  E)   None of the above

Questions 25 and 26 refer to the following: a container contains a large unspecified number of ping-pong balls. A student takes 60 balls from the container, marks them with a blue dot, returns the marked balls to the container, and thoroughly mixes the balls. She then takes 60 balls again from the container. Of these, 12 have blue dots. She now wants to use this data to estimate the total number of ping-pong balls in the container.

(I) 25.   The method described in this example is called

    A)   a census.
    B)   a survey.
    C)   capture-recapture.
    D)   controlled study.
    E)   None of the above

(I) 26.   An estimate for the number of ping-pong balls in the container is

    A)   100.
    B)   300.
    C)   500.
    D)   600.
    E)   None of the above

Questions 27 through 29 refer to the capture-recapture method: n_1 denotes the size of the tagged (captured) sample; n_2 denotes the size of the second (recaptured) sample, and k denotes the number of tagged individuals in the second sample.

(I) 27.   If $n_1 = 250$, $n_2 = 150$, and $k = 25$, an estimate for the size of the population is

    A)   15.
    B)   1500.
    C)   2500.
    D)   3000.
    E)   None of the above

(I) 28.   If $n_1 = 32$, $n_2 = 50$, and $k = 8$, the N-value of the population is approximately

    A)   320.
    B)   256.
    C)   200.
    D)   30.
    E)   None of the above

(I) 29.   If $n_1 = 135$, $n_2 = 116$, and $k = 15$, the estimated size of the population is approximately

    A)   1044.
    B)   1012.
    C)   973.
    D)   861.
    E)   None of the above

(I) 30. A researcher interested in Cleansburg citizens' attitudes toward a revitalized downtown area surveys a randomly selected group of 200 downtown office workers. 66% of those surveyed indicated they are in favor of revitalizing the downtown area. The researcher concluded that "about two thirds of the people in Cleansburg are in favor of revitalizing the downtown area." This conclusion might be invalid because

     A)   there was no control group.
     B)   66% is not exactly two thirds.
     C)   the sample is not representative of the population.
     D)   the size of the sample is too small.
     E)   None of the above

(I) 31. Any data collection process in which the data are collected from each and every member of the population is called

     A)   a parameter.
     B)   a public opinion poll.
     C)   a survey.
     D)   a census.
     E)   None of the above

(I) 32. Any data collection process in which the data are collected from a selected subgroup of the population is called

     A)   a parameter.
     B)   a statistic.
     C)   a survey.
     D)   a census.
     E)   None of the above

(I) 33. Simple random sampling means that

     A)   every member of the population has a chance of being in the sample.
     B)   all members of the population have an equal chance of being in the sample.
     C)   every member of the population is automatically a member of the sample.
     D)   any two groups of members of the population of equal size have the same chance of being in the sample.
     E)   None of the above

(I) 34. A method of sampling in which the population is broken up into categories and the members of the sample are chosen randomly from within some group of randomly selected categories is called

     A)   stratified sampling.
     B)   quota sampling.
     C)   simple random sampling.
     D)   randomized controlled sampling.
     E)   None of the above

(I) 35. The primary reason for having a control group and a treatment group in a clinical study is

     A)   to save money.
     B)   to eliminate confounding variables.
     C)   to make it easier to collect the data.
     D)   to combat the placebo effect.
     E)   None of the above

(I) 36. Any type of numerical information about a population obtained from a sample is called

A)   a parameter.
B)   a statistic.
C)   a controlled experiment.
D)   a clinical study.
E)   None of the above

(I) 37. A controlled placebo experiment is said to be blind when

A)   the members of the control group are told they are in the treatment group.
B)   the members of the treatment group are told they are in the control group.
C)   neither the members of the control group nor the members of the treatment group know to which of the two groups they belong.
D)   none of the scientists conducting the experiment know which patients are in the control group and which patients are in the treatment group.
E)   None of the above

(I) 38. A controlled placebo experiment is said to be double blind when

A)   the members of the control group are told they are in the treatment group and vice versa.
B)   neither the members of the control group nor the members of the treatment group know to which of the two groups they belong.
C)   none of the scientists conducting the experiment know which patients are in the control group and which patients are in the treatment groups.
D)   neither the subject nor the scientists conducting the experiment know which individuals are in the treatment group and which are in the control group.
E)   None of the above

(I) 39. Which of the following [A), B), C), or D)] is **not** required in a double-blind placebo experiment?

A)   That there be a control group and a treatment group.
B)   That the size of the control group and treatment group be the same.
C)   That neither the members of the control group nor the members of the treatment group know to which of the two groups they belong.
D)   That the scientists conducting the experiment do not know which individuals are in the treatment group and which are in the control group.
E)   None of the above

(I) 40. The sampling method currently used in public opinion polls is called

A)   simple random sampling.
B)   quota sampling.
C)   stratified sampling.
D)   capture-recapture sampling.
E)   None of the above

Chapter 14: Descriptive Statistics

Questions 1 through 8 refer to the following frequency table. The table shows the scores of a group of students on a 10 point multiple choice placement test.

Exam Score	Frequency
3	5
4	3
5	5
6	2
7	7
8	6
9	1
10	1

(I)   1.   The total number of students taking the test is

   A)   52.
   B)   8.
   C)   30.
   D)   180.
   E)   None of the above

(I)   2.   The average score on the test is

   A)   5.
   B)   6.
   C)   5.5.
   D)   6.5.
   E)   None of the above

(I)   3.   The median score on the test is

   A)   5.5.
   B)   6.
   C)   5.
   D)   6.5.
   E)   None of the above

(I)   4.   The first quartile on the test is

   A)   4.
   B)   5.5.
   C)   4.5.
   D)   5.
   E)   None of the above

(I)   5.   The third quartile on the test is

   A)   6.5.
   B)   7.5.
   C)   7.
   D)   8.
   E)   None of the above

(I)   6.   The range on the test is

      A)   7.
      B)   9.
      C)   8.
      D)   10.
      E)   None of the above

(I)   7.   What kind of variable is the test score?

      A)   qualitative and discrete
      B)   qualitative and continuous
      C)   quantitative and discrete
      D)   quantitative and continuous
      E)   None of the above

Questions 8 through 13 refer to the following example. The scores on a 30 point multiple choice exam are given in the following frequency table:

Exam Score	Frequency
23	6
24	6
25	4
26	1
27	6
28	6
29	4
30	1

(I)   8.   The average score on the exam is

      A)   25.
      B)   26.
      C)   25.5.
      D)   26.5.
      E)   None of the above

(I)   9.   The median score on the exam is

      A)   25.5.
      B)   26.
      C)   25.
      D)   26.5.
      E)   None of the above

(I) 10.   The first quartile on the exam is

      A)   24.
      B)   25.5.
      C)   24.5.
      D)   25.
      E)   None of the above

(I) 11.   The third quartile on the exam is

      A)   26.5.
      B)   27.5.
      C)   27.
      D)   28.
      E)   None of the above

(I)   12.   The range on the exam is

    A)   7.
    B)   9.
    C)   8.
    D)   10.
    E)   None of the above

(I)   13.   The inter quartile range on the exam is

    A)   2.
    B)   3.
    C)   2.5.
    D)   3.5.
    E)   None of the above

Questions 14 through 16 refer to the following data set: $\{-2, -3, 1, 8\}$.

(I)   14.   The average of the four numbers is

    A)   4.
    B)   3.5.
    C)   1.
    D)   0.25.
    E)   None of the above

(I)   15.   The median of the four numbers is

    A)   −1.
    B)   −0.5.
    C)   0.
    D)   2.
    E)   None of the above

(II)   16.   The standard deviation of the four numbers is

    A) $\sqrt{12.5}$.
    B) $\sqrt{18.5}$.
    C) $\sqrt{19.5}$.
    D) $\sqrt{22.5}$.
    E)   None of the above

Questions 17 through 19 refer to the following data set: $\{-1, -3, -5, 9\}$.

(I)   17.   The average of the four numbers is

    A)   1.
    B)   −1.
    C)   0.
    D)   0.25.
    E)   None of the above

(I)   18.   The median of the four numbers is

    A)   −4.
    B)   −2.
    C)   0.
    D)   1.
    E)   None of the above

(II)   19.   The standard deviation of the four numbers is approximately

     A)   10.77.
     B)   5.385.
     C)   29.
     D)   116.
     E)   None of the above

Questions 20 through 22 refer to a data set consisting of 251 numbers.

(I)   20.   After sorting the data set (in increasing order from left to right), the median is

     A)   the number in the 125th position.
     B)   the number in the 126th position.
     C)   the average of the numbers in the 125th and 126th positions.
     D)   the sum of all the numbers divided by 251.
     E)   None of the above

(I)   21.   After sorting the data set (in increasing order from left to right), the first quartile is

     A)   the number in the 63rd position.
     B)   the number in the 64th position.
     C)   the average of the numbers in the 63rd and 64th positions.
     D)   the average of the numbers in the 62nd and 63rd positions.
     E)   None of the above

(I)   22.   After sorting the data set (in increasing order from left to right), the third quartile is

     A)   the number in the 63rd position counting backwards from the right.
     B)   the number in the 64th position counting backwards from the right.
     C)   the average of the numbers in the 63rd and 64th positions counting backwards from the right.
     D)   the sum of the median plus the first quartile.
     E)   None of the above

Questions 23 through 26 refer to the following figure. The data represents the annual salaries of 200 professional musicians.

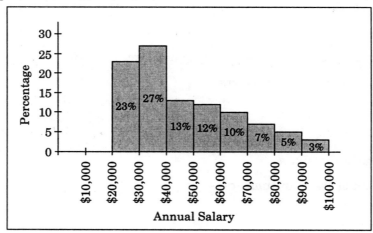

(I)   23.   The kind of graph shown in the figure is called

     A)   a bar graph.
     B)   a histogram.
     C)   a frequency graph.
     D)   a box plot.
     E)   None of the above

(I) 24. Approximately how many musicians make $40,000 or less?

    A) 100
    B) 54
    C) 50
    D) 27
    E) None of the above

(I) 25. The median salary of this group of musicians is approximately

    A) $80,000.
    B) $50,000.
    C) $60,000.
    D) $40,000.
    E) None of the above.

(I) 26. The third quartile of the salaries of this group of musicians is approximately

    A) $60,000.
    B) $70,000.
    C) $75,000.
    D) $80,000.
    E) None of the above.

Questions 27 through 30 refer to the following figure. The box plots represent a comparison of the annual salaries of a group of opera and a group of country western singers respectively.

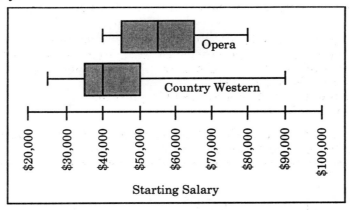

(I) 27. Which of the following represents the five number summary for the salaries of the opera singers?

    A) Min = $20,000, Q_1 = $40,000, Q_2 = $55,000, Q_3 = $80,000, Max = $100,000
    B) Min = $40,000, Q_1 = $45,000, Q_2 = $55,000, Q_3 = $65,000, Max = $80,000
    C) Min = $45,000, Q_1 = $55,000, Q_2 = $55,000, Q_3 = $55,000, Max = $65,000
    D) Min = $0, Q_1 = $40,000, Q_2 = $45,000, Q_3 = $55,000, Max = $65,000
    E) None of the above

(I) 28. The range of salaries for the group of country western singers is approximately

    A) $15,000.
    B) $40,000.
    C) $65,000.
    D) $90,000.
    E) None of the above.

(I) 29. The interquartile range of salaries for the group of country western singers is

    A) $10,000.
    B) $15,000.
    C) $40,000.
    D) $50,000.
    E) None of the above.

(I) 30. Reba is a country western singer whose annual salary is twice the median salary of the group of country western singers. Sylvia is the highest paid among the group of opera singers. Which of the following statements is true?

    A) Sylvia's annual salary is higher than Reba's.
    B) Reba's annual salary is higher than Sylvia's.
    C) Reba and Sylvia have the same annual salary.
    D) The information provided is not sufficient to determine which of the two salaries is higher.
    E) None of the above.

(I) 31. A class consisting of 120 students is given an exam. The first quartile for the scores on the exam is 62. This means that

    A) 30 students scored 62 or higher.
    B) 0 students scored 62 or higher.
    C) 90 students scored 62 or higher.
    D) 100 students scored 62 or higher.
    E) None of the above

(II) 32. The average of a data set consisting of 11 numbers is 8. The smallest of the numbers is Min = 5. If Max is the largest of the numbers in the data set, which of the following could be a possible value of Max?

    A) 39
    B) 8.1
    C) 8.2
    D) 8.3
    E) None of the above

(I) 33. The standard deviation of a set of 100 numbers is 0. Which of the following statements must be true about the set of numbers?

    A) All of the numbers must be 0.
    B) All of the numbers must be positive or zero.
    C) Half of the numbers must be positive or zero and half of the numbers must be negative or zero.
    D) All of the numbers must be equal.
    E) None of the above

(I) 34. What is the size relationship between the average and the median of a data set?

    A) The average is always more than the median.
    B) The average is always less than the median.
    C) The average is always equal to the median.
    D) The average can be smaller than, equal to, or bigger than the median.
    E) None of the above

(I) 35. When the possible values of a numerical variable change by minimum increments, the variable is called

    A) continuous.
    B) discrete.
    C) categorical.
    D) qualitative.
    E) None of the above

(I) 36. Which of the following is the most appropriate type of graph for representing a continuous random variable?

A)   a pictogram
B)   a bar graph
C)   a pie chart
D)   a histogram
E)   None of the above.

(I) 37. Which of the following [A), B), C), or D)] is **not** part of the five-number summary of a data set?

A)   the smallest value in the data set
B)   the median of the data set
C)   the first quartile of the data set
D)   the average of the data set
E)   All of the above are given in the five-number summary.

(I) 38. Which of the following [A), B), C), or D)] can **never** be a negative number?

A)   the mean of a data set
B)   the median of a data set
C)   the standard deviation of a data set
D)   the maximum value of a data set
E)   All of the above can be negative numbers.

(I) 39. Which of the following [A), B), C), or D)] is **not** a measure of spread?

A)   the median
B)   the range
C)   the interquartile range
D)   the standard deviation
E)   All of the above are measures of spread.

(I) 40. Suppose that the data set $\{x_1, x_2, x_3, \cdots, x_N\}$ has average A and standard deviation s. If A' and s' are the average and standard deviation of the data set $\{x_1 + c, x_2 + c, x_3 + c, \cdots, x_N + c\}$ respectively, then

A) $A' = A + c$ and $s' = s + c$.
B) $A' = A$ and $s' = s + c$.
C) $A' = A + c$ and $s' = s$.
D) $A' = A$ and $s' = s$.
E)   None of the above

Chapter 15: Measuring Uncertainty

(I)   1.   A coin is tossed twice. The sample space for this random experiment is

A)   {H, T}
B)   {H, H, T, T}
C)   {HH, HT, TH, TT}
D)   {HH, HT, TT}
E)   None of the above

(I)   2.   If an honest coin is tossed twice, the probability that both tosses will come up heads is

A) $\frac{3}{4}$.
B) $\frac{1}{2}$.
C) $\frac{1}{3}$.
D) $\frac{1}{4}$.
E)   None of the above

(I)   3.   If an honest coin is tossed twice, the probability that at least one of the tosses will come up heads is

A) $\frac{3}{4}$.
B) $\frac{1}{2}$.
C) $\frac{1}{3}$.
D) $\frac{1}{4}$.
E)   None of the above

(I)   4.   If an honest coin is tossed twice, the probability of both tosses coming up the same is

A) $\frac{3}{4}$.
B) $\frac{1}{2}$.
C) $\frac{1}{3}$.
D) $\frac{1}{4}$.
E)   None of the above

(I)   5.   A coin is tossed three times. Which of the following describes the sample space for this random experiment?

A)   {3 H's, 2 H's and 1 T, 1 H and 2 T's, 3 T's}
B)   {H, T}
C)   {HHH, TTT}
D)   {$HHH, HHT, HTH, THH, HTT, THT, TTH, TTT$}
E)   None of the above

(I)   6.   If an honest coin is tossed three times, the probability of tossing 3 heads is

A) $\frac{1}{2}$.
B) $\frac{1}{4}$.
C) $\frac{1}{8}$.
D) $\frac{3}{8}$.
E)   None of the above

(I)   7.   A coin is tossed 5 times. How many different outcomes are there in the sample space?

 A) 32
 B) 25
 C) 10
 D) 2
 E) None of the above

(I)   8.   A coin is tossed ten times. How many different outcomes are there in the sample space?

 A) 10
 B) 20
 C) 2^{10}
 D) 10^2
 E) None of the above

(I)   9.   An honest coin is tossed ten times. The probability of tossing one head and nine tails is

 A) $\frac{1}{1024}$.
 B) $\frac{10}{1024}$.
 C) $\frac{1}{10}$.
 D) $\frac{1}{9}$.
 E) None of the above

(I)   10.   An honest coin is tossed ten times. The probability that the number of heads is double the number of tails is

 A) 0.
 B) $\frac{1}{2}$.
 C) $\frac{1}{3}$.
 D) $\frac{2}{3}$.
 E) None of the above

(II)   11.   Suppose that an honest coin is tossed 10 times. What is the probability that at least once it comes up heads?

 A) $\frac{9}{10}$
 B) $\frac{1023}{1024}$
 C) $\frac{1}{2}$
 D) $\frac{10}{9}$
 E) None of the above

Questions 12 through 18 refer to the roll of a pair of honest dice.

(I)   12.   How many different outcomes are there in the sample space?

 A) 6
 B) 12
 C) 30
 D) 64
 E) None of the above

(I) 13. Which of the following [A), B), C), or D)] is **not** an outcome in the sample space?

A) (1,1)
B) (4,5)
C) (5,2)
D) (6,6)
E) All of the above are outcomes in the sample space.

(I) 14. What is the probability of rolling a total of 12?

A) $\frac{1}{36}$
B) $\frac{2}{36}$
C) $\frac{1}{6}$
D) $\frac{2}{6}$
E) None of the above

(I) 15. What is the probability of rolling a total of 7?

A) $\frac{1}{36}$
B) 7/36
C) $\frac{1}{6}$
D) $\frac{2}{6}$
E) None of the above

(I) 16. What is the probability of rolling a total of 11?

A) $\frac{1}{6}$
B) $\frac{1}{36}$
C) $\frac{2}{36}$
D) $\frac{9}{36}$
E) None of the above

(I) 17. What is the probability of rolling a total of either 7 or 11?

A) $\frac{1}{6}$
B) $\frac{1}{36}$
C) $\frac{2}{36}$
D) $\frac{9}{36}$
E) None of the above

(II) 18. What is the probability of rolling a total that is neither 7 nor 11?

A) $\frac{28}{36}$
B) $\frac{30}{36}$
C) $\frac{34}{36}$
D) $\frac{18}{36}$
E) None of the above

(II) 19.   Two cards are drawn in order from a well shuffled deck of 52 cards. The probability that both cards are hearts is given by

A) $\left(\frac{13}{52}\right) \times \left(\frac{13}{51}\right)$.

B) $\left(\frac{13}{52}\right) \times \left(\frac{12}{52}\right)$.

C) $\left(\frac{13}{52}\right) \times \left(\frac{12}{51}\right)$.

D) $\left(\frac{13}{52}\right)$.

E)   None of the above

(II) 20.   Two cards are drawn in order from a well shuffled deck of 52 cards. The probability that both cards are 10's is given by

A) $\left(\frac{4}{52}\right) \times \left(\frac{3}{51}\right)$.

B) $\left(\frac{4}{52}\right) \times \left(\frac{3}{52}\right)$.

C) $\left(\frac{4}{52}\right) \times \left(\frac{4}{51}\right)$.

D) $\left(\frac{4}{52}\right)^{2}$.

E)   None of the above

Questions 21 through 24 refer to the following example: A computer password consists of any five capital letters from the ordinary English alphabet (A through Z).

(I) 21.   How many different passwords are possible?

A)   26
B) 26×5
C) 26^{5}
D) $26 \times 25 \times 24 \times 23 \times 22$
E)   None of the above

(I) 22.   How many of the passwords have no repeated letters?

A)   26
B) 26×5
C) 26^{5}
D) $26 \times 25 \times 24 \times 23 \times 22$
E)   None of the above

(II) 23.   How many of the passwords start with the letter Z?

A) 26^{4}
B) $26^{5} - 1$
C) 26×25
D) 25^{4}
E)   None of the above

(II) 24.   How many of the passwords start with the letter Z and end with the letter W?

A) 24^{5}
B) $26 \times 25 \times 24^{3}$
C) 24^{3}
D) 26^{3}
E)   None of the above

Questions 25 through 28 refer to the following example: Tasmanian automobile license plates consist of three capital letters (A through Z) followed by three digits (0 through 9).

(I) 25. How many different Tasmanian license plates are possible?

A) $26^3 + 10^3$
B) $26^3 \times 10^3$
C) 36^6
D) $(26 \times 3) + (10 \times 3)$
E) None of the above

(I) 26. How many Tasmanian license plates end with a 1?

A) $26^3 \times 10^3$
B) $26^3 \times 10^2$
C) $26^3 \times 10^3 - 1$
D) $26^2 \times 10^3$
E) None of the above

(II) 27. How many Tasmanian license plates start with the word ZOO?

A) 1000
B) 100
C) 10
D) 1
E) None of the above

(II) 28. How many Tasmanian license plates have no repeated symbols (different letters and different digits)?

A) $\left(26^3 - 1\right) \times \left(10^3 - 1\right)$
B) $26 \times 25 \times 24 \times 23 \times 22 \times 21$
C) $26 \times 25 \times 24$
D) $26 \times 25 \times 24 \times 10 \times 9 \times 8$
E) None of the above

Questions 29 through 34 refer to the following example: A computer password is made up of five characters. Each character can be a capital letter (A through Z) or a digit (0 through 9).

(I) 29. How many different such computer passwords are there?

A) $26^5 + 10^5$
B) 36×5
C) 5^{36}
D) 36^5
E) None of the above

(I) 30. How many do not start with the digit 0?

A) 35×36^4
B) 35^5
C) $36^5 - 1$
D) 36^4
E) None of the above

(I) 31.   How many start with a digit?

A) 10×26^4
B) 10×35^4
C) 10×36^4
D) 36^4
E)   None of the above

(I) 32.   How many consist entirely of letters?

A) 26^5
B) $26 \times 25 \times 24 \times 23 \times 22$
C) 5^{26}
D) 26×5
E)   None of the above

(II) 33.   How many have 4 letters and only one digit?

A) $26^4 \times 10$
B) $5 \times 26^4 \times 10$
C) $4 \times 26 \times 10$
D) $26 \times 25 \times 24 \times 23 \times 10$
E)   None of the above

(II) 34.   How many have 3 letters and 2 digits?

A) $26^3 \times 10^2$
B) $26 \times 25 \times 24 \times 10 \times 9$
C) $3 \times 26^3 \times 10^2$
D) $10 \times 26^3 \times 10^2$
E)   None of the above

(I) 35. $_9P_3 =$

A)   750
B)   504
C)   320
D)   264
E)   None of the above

(I) 36. $_{10}P_{10} =$

A)   1
B) 10^2
C)   10!
D) $\frac{10!}{10! \, 0!}$
E)   None of the above

(I) 37. $_7C_4 =$

A)   60
B)   35
C)   16
D)   10
E)   None of the above

(I)   38. $_{100}C_{100} =$

     A)   0
     B)   1
     C)   100
     D)   100!
     E)   None of the above

(II)   39.   A Tasmanian lottery ticket consists of choosing 8 different numbers between 10 and 62. The number of possible lottery tickets is given by

     A) $\frac{53}{8}$

     B) $\frac{62!}{54!}$

     C) $\frac{53!}{8! \, 45!}$

     D) $\frac{62!}{8! \, 54!}$

     E)   None of the above

Questions 40 and 41 refer to the following example: Four basketball teams called $A, B, C,$ and D are entered in a tournament. According to the odds makers, the probability that team A will win the tournament is $\Pr(A) = 0.1$, and the other three teams all have an equal probability of winning the tournament.

(I)   40.   What is the probability that team A will **not** win the tournament?

     A)   0.9
     B)   0.4
     C)   0.3
     D)   Cannot be determined from the information given.
     E)   None of the above

(I)   41.   What is the probability that team D will win the tournament?

     A)   0.25
     B)   0.3
     C)   0.45
     D)   0.9
     E)   None of the above

Questions 42 through 44 refer to the following example: A French restaurant offers a menu consisting of 5 different appetizers, 3 different salads, 2 different soups, 7 different main courses, and 3 different desserts. The restaurant offers different combinations of "fixed price dinners" on different days of the week.

(I)   42.   On Mondays through Thursdays, the "fixed price dinner" consists of a choice of appetizer, a soup, a main course, and a dessert. Assuming you don't pass on any of these, how many different "fixed price dinners" are possible on these days?

     A)   210
     B)   70
     C)   42
     D)   17
     E)   None of the above

(I)   43.   On Fridays and Saturdays, the "fixed price dinner" consists of a choice of appetizer, a choice of either soup or salad, a main course, and a dessert. Assuming you don't pass on any of these, how many different "fixed price dinners" are possible on Fridays and Saturdays?

      A)   20
      B)   21
      C)   525
      D)   630
      E)   None of the above

(I)   44.   On Sundays, the "fixed price dinner" consists of a main course, a dessert, and any two of the other three types of items (i.e., appetizer and soup, or appetizer and salad, or soup and salad). Assuming you don't pass on any of these, how many "fixed price dinners" are possible on Sundays?

      A)   5880
      B)   651
      C)   420
      D)   30
      E)   None of the above

(I)   45.   If the chances of rain tomorrow are 30%, then the odds of rain tomorrow can be given as

      A)   3 to 10.
      B)   3 to 7.
      C)   3 to 13.
      D)   3 to 1.
      E)   None of the above

(I)   46.   Suppose that the odds of winning the grand prize in a raffle are 1 to 15. What is the probability of winning the grand prize?

      A) $\frac{1}{14}$
      B) $\frac{1}{15}$
      C) $\frac{1}{16}$
      D) $\frac{14}{15}$
      E)   None of the above

(I)   47.   Suppose that there are 500 children living at the Pinedale Orphanage. If on a given day there is a child who has a birthday then it's "cake" day (everyone gets a piece of birthday cake for dessert). If on a given day there is more than one child who has a birthday, then it's a "cake and ice cream" day. What is the probability that a whole year can go by without any "cake and ice cream" days?

      A)   1
      B) $\frac{1}{2}$
      C) $\frac{2}{365}$
      D)   0
      E)   None of the above

Questions 48 through 50 refer to the following example: A couple is planning to have four children. Suppose that for this couple, the probability of a boy is 46% and the probability of a girl is 54%. (Assume the gender of each child is independent from that of the other children.)

(II)   48.   What is the probability that they will have four boys?

A) 0.46^4
B) $0.46^3 \times 0.54$
C) $0.46 + 0.46 + 0.46 + 0.46$
D) $\frac{1}{4}$
E)   All of the above are random experiments.

(II)   49.   What is the probability that they will have one girl and three boys?

A) $4 \times 0.46^3 \times 0.54$
B) $0.46^3 \times 0.54$
C) $0.54 + 0.46 + 0.46 + 0.46$
D) $\frac{1}{4}$
E)   All of the above are random experiments.

(III)   50.   What is the probability that they will have an equal number of girls and boys?

A) $6 \times 0.46^2 \times 0.54^2$
B) $4 \times 0.46^2 \times 0.54^2$
C) $0.46^2 \times 0.54^2$
D) $0.46^2 + 0.54^2$
E)   All of the above are random experiments.

(I)   51.   Which of the following [A), B), C), or D)] is **not** a random experiment?

A)   predicting the winner of next year's world series
B)   tossing a coin
C)   rolling a pair of dice
D)   drawing a card from a deck of cards
E)   All of the above are random experiments.

(I)   52.   In a general probability model, which of the following statements [A), B), C), or D)] is **not** true?

A)   All probabilities are between 0 and 1 (0 and 1 included).
B)   All probabilities are equal.
C)   The impossible event always has probability equal to 0.
D)   The probability of the sample space is always equal to 1.
E)   All of the above statements are true.

Chapter 16: Normal Distributions

Questions 1 through 12 refer to the following: 150 students in a math class take the final exam. The scores on the exam have an approximately normal distribution with center $\mu = 65$ and standard deviation $\sigma = 10$.

(I)   1.   The number of students scoring 65 points or more is approximately

      A)   50.
      B)   75.
      C)   65.
      D)   95.
      E)   None of the above

(I)   2.   The average score on the exam was approximately

      A)   50.
      B)   65.
      C)   75.
      D)   10.
      E)   None of the above

(I)   3.   Approximately 95% of the class scored between

      A)   45 and 85.
      B)   0 and 85.
      C)   35 and 95.
      D)   65 and 85.
      E)   None of the above

(I)   4.   Assuming there were no outliers, the lowest score on the exam was around

      A)   65.
      B)   35.
      C)   10.
      D)   0.
      E)   None of the above

(I)   5.   Approximately what percent of the students scored between 65 and 75 points?

      A)   10%
      B)   34%
      C)   68%
      D)   95%
      E)   None of the above

(I)   6.   Peter's score on the exam places him in the 16th percentile of the class. Peter's score on the exam is approximately

      A)   55
      B)   45
      C)   35
      D)   16
      E)   None of the above

(I)   7.   Carol scored 75 points on the exam. In approximately what percentile of the class does this score place her?

      A)   34th percentile
      B)   68th percentile
      C)   84th percentile
      D)   95th percentile
      E)   None of the above

(I)   8.   The third quartile of the scores on the exam is approximately

A)   67 points.
B)   72 points.
C)   80 points.
D)   84 points.
E)   None of the above

(I)   9.   A score of 85 corresponds to a standardized value of

A)   20.
B)   8.5.
C)   2.
D)   −2.
E)   None of the above

(II)   10.   A score of 50 corresponds to a standardized value of

A)   −1.5.
B)   −5.
C)   5.
D)   1.5.
E)   None of the above

(I)   11.   Approximately what percentage of the test scores had standardized values between −2 and 2?

A)   50%
B)   68%
C)   95%
D)   99%
E)   None of the above

(III) 12.   Approximately how many students had test scores with standardized values between −0.675 and 1?

A)   37
B)   75
C)   88
D)   140
E)   None of the above

Questions 13 through 20 refer to the following: As part of a study on the metabolism of athletes, 400 college basketball players are randomly chosen and their weights taken. The distribution of the weights is approximately normal. The average weight is 215 pounds and the standard deviation is 15 pounds.

(I)   13.   Of the 400 players, approximately how many weighed 200 pounds or less?

A)   32
B)   64
C)   100
D)   336
E)   None of the above

(I)   14.   Assuming there were no outliers, the range of weights was approximately

A)   60 pounds.
B)   90 pounds.
C)   180 pounds.
D)   400 pounds.
E)   None of the above

(I)   15.   The first quartile of the weights was approximately

      A)   225 pounds.
      B)   208 pounds.
      C)   205 pounds.
      D)   200 pounds.
      E)   None of the above

(I)   16.   Approximately how many players weighed over 225 pounds?

      A)   75
      B)   100
      C)   84
      D)   64
      E)   None of the above

(I)   17.   A weight of 185 pounds corresponds to a standardized value of

      A)   −1.
      B)   −2.
      C)   −3.
      D)   4.
      E)   None of the above

(II) 18.   A weight of 257 pounds corresponds to a standardized value of

      A)   2.8.
      B)   1.8.
      C)   −1.5.
      D)   −1.8.
      E)   None of the above

(II) 19.   Approximately how many players had weights between 215 and 225 pounds?

      A)   100
      B)   50
      C)   25
      D)   20
      E)   None of the above

(III) 20.   Approximately how many players had weights with standardized values between 1 and 2?

      A)   108
      B)   190
      C)   200
      D)   216
      E)   None of the above

Questions 21 through 25 refer to the following normal curve, with center μ and standard deviation σ.

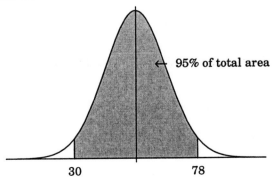

95% of total area

30   78

(I) 21. $\mu =$

   A)   54
   B)   48
   C)   39
   D)   12
   E)   None of the above

(I) 22. $\sigma =$

   A)   48
   B)   24
   C)   12
   D)   6
   E)   None of the above

(I) 23.   A data value of 90 corresponds to a standardized value of

   A)   36.
   B)   12.
   C)   3.
   D)   2.
   E)   None of the above

(I) 24.   A data value of 30 corresponds to a standardized value of

   A)   −2.
   B)   −1.
   C)   1.
   D)   2.
   E)   None of the above

(II) 25.   A data value of 39 corresponds to a standardized value of

   A)   −1.5.
   B)   −1.25.
   C)   1.25.
   D)   1.5.
   E)   None of the above

Questions 26 through 30 refer to the following normal curve, with center μ and standard deviation σ.

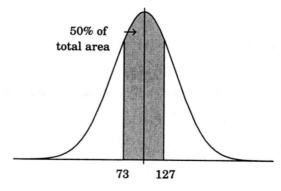

50% of total area

73   127

(I) 26. $Q_2 =$

   A)   27
   B)   40
   C)   54
   D)   100
   E)   None of the above

(I)   27. $\sigma =$

      A)   27
      B)   40
      C)   54
      D)   100
      E)   None of the above

(I)   28. $Q_1 =$

      A)   50
      B)   73
      C)   100
      D)   127
      E)   None of the above

(I)   29.   A data value of 60 corresponds to a standardized value of

      A)   −2.
      B)   −1.
      C)   −40.
      D)   0.
      E)   None of the above

(II)   30.   If the standardized value of x is 0.5, then $x =$

      A)   80.
      B)   100.
      C)   120.
      D)   147.
      E)   None of the above

Questions 31 through 35 refer to a normal distribution described by the following figure. The mean is μ and the standard deviation is σ.

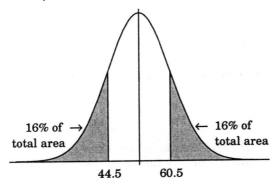

(I)   31. $\mu =$

      A)   52.5
      B)   50
      C)   48.5
      D)   32
      E)   None of the above

(I)   32. $\sigma =$

      A)   2
      B)   4
      C)   8
      D)   10
      E)   None of the above

(I)   33.   What is the approximate value of Q_3?

A)   55.2
B)   57.9
C)   65.7
D)   75
E)   None of the above

(II)   34.   A data value of 40.5 corresponds to a standardized value of

A)   12.
B)   0.
C)   −1.
D)   −1.5.
E)   None of the above

(II)   35.   If the standardized value of x is −1.25, then $x =$

A)   51.25.
B)   42.5.
C)   62.5.
D)   65.
E)   None of the above

Questions 36 through 40 refer to the following: Over the last 80 years records have been
kept of the annual rainfall in the Tasmanian desert. The distribution of annual rainfall is
approximately normal and has no outliers. The minimum of 4.5 inches of rain occurred in
1952; the maximum of 11.7 inches of rain occurred in 1934.

(I)   36.   What is the approximate average annual rainfall over the last 80 years?

A)   8.1 inches
B)   7.2 inches
C)   3.6 inches
D)   1.2 inches
E)   None of the above

(I)   37.   The standard deviation of the rainfall distribution is approximately

A)   7.2 inches.
B)   3.6 inches.
C)   1.8 inches.
D)   1.2 inches.
E)   None of the above

(I)   38.   In this part of the world, anything over 10.5 inches of annual rainfall is considered
              a "wet" year. Of the last 80 years, approximately how many were "wet" ones?

A)   2
B)   4
C)   6
D)   16
E)   None of the above

(II)   39.   Two years ago, the annual rainfall was 7.5 inches. The standardized value
              corresponding to this rainfall is approximately

A)   2.5.
B)   1.
C)   0.
D)   −0.5.
E)   None of the above

(II) 40. The third quartile of the rainfall distribution is approximately

   A) 8.9 inches.
   B) 8.1 inches.
   C) 7.3 inches.
   D) 7 inches.
   E) None of the above

Questions 41 through 44 refer to the following: For a population of 2000 students taking the SAT math exam, the scores on the exam have an approximately normal distribution with center $\mu = 590$ and standard deviation $\sigma = 70$.

(I) 41. Approximately how many students scored between 450 and 730?

   A) 1950
   B) 1900
   C) 1360
   D) 1994
   E) None of the above

(I) 42. Approximately how many students scored less than 543 points?

   A) 500
   B) 543
   C) 637
   D) 750
   E) None of the above

(II) 43. The third quartile of the scores on the exam is approximately

   A) 660.
   B) 637.
   C) 607.
   D) 543.
   E) None of the above

(II) 44. A score of 700 has an approximate standardized value of

   A) 10.
   B) 1.57.
   C) −1.57.
   D) 110.
   E) None of the above

(I) 45. The standard deviation of a normal distribution is $\sigma = 20$. What is the interquartile range for this distribution?

   A) 6.75
   B) 13.5
   C) 27
   D) 33.75
   E) None of the above

(I) 46. If μ is the center and σ is the standard deviation of a normal distribution, then which of the following statements is true?

   A) μ and σ must always be positive numbers.
   B) μ must always be bigger than σ.
   C) μ must always be positive, σ can be positive or negative.
   D) σ must always be positive, μ can be positive or negative.
   E) None of the above

Questions 47 through 50 refer to the following example: An honest coin is tossed 1600 times. The random variable X denotes the total number of heads that come up in the 1600 tosses.

(I)   47.   What are the chances that X is 800 or less?

     A)   approximately 50%
     B)   approximately 40%
     C)   approximately 0%
     D)   approximately 100%
     E)   None of the above

(I)   48.   What are the chances that X is between 780 and 820?

     A)   approximately 34%
     B)   approximately 68%
     C)   approximately 80%
     D)   approximately 95%
     E)   None of the above

(I)   49.   What are the chances that X is less than 600?

     A)   approximately 16%
     B)   approximately 25%
     C)   approximately 32%
     D)   approximately 0%
     E)   None of the above

(I)   50.   What are the chances that X is more than 813?

     A)   approximately 16%
     B)   approximately 25%
     C)   approximately 75%
     D)   approximately 84%
     E)   None of the above

Answers

CHAPTER 1		CHAPTER 2		CHAPTER 3		CHAPTER 4	
1.	D	1.	A	1.	D	1.	B
2.	A	2.	C	2.	B	2.	A
3.	C	3.	C	3.	C	3.	C
4.	A	4.	C	4.	A	4.	B
5.	B	5.	D	5.	B	5.	C
6.	A	6.	B	6.	A	6.	D
7.	B	7.	D	7.	D	7.	A
8.	C	8.	C	8.	B	8.	B
9.	B	9.	C	9.	D	9.	D
10.	B	10.	B	10.	E	10.	C
11.	D	11.	E	11.	C	11.	A
12.	A	12.	B	12.	B	12.	D
13.	C	13.	C	13.	E	13.	B
14.	B	14.	C	14.	C	14.	A
15.	D	15.	C	15.	B	15.	B
16.	C	16.	D	16.	D	16.	A
17.	A	17.	B	17.	B	17.	C
18.	A	18.	B	18.	C	18.	A
19.	D	19.	C	19.	C	19.	D
20.	B	20.	C	20.	A	20.	A
21.	B	21.	D	21.	B	21.	C
22.	C	22.	A	22.	D	22.	B
23.	A	23.	B	23.	B	23.	B
24.	A	24.	B	24.	B	24.	B
25.	D	25.	A	25.	B	25.	D
26.	D	26.	B	26.	A	26.	C
27.	D	27.	C	27.	D	27.	B
28.	B	28.	C	28.	D	28.	A
29.	B	29.	C	29.	A	29.	C
30.	A	30.	B	30.	C	30.	D
31.	C	31.	A	31.	C	31.	B
32.	B	32.	B	32.	C	32.	B
33.	D	33.	D	33.	A	33.	C
34.	C	34.	A	34.	D	34.	B
35.	B	35.	A	35.	A	35.	A
36.	C	36.	D	36.	A	36.	C
37.	A	37.	B	37.	B	37.	D
38.	B	38.	C	38.	D	38.	A
39.	B	39.	C	39.	E	39.	A
40.	D	40.	C	40.	E	40.	B
41.	C	41.	A	41.	C	41.	A
42.	A	42.	A	42.	E	42.	C
43.	B	43.	D	43.	B	43.	B
44.	E	44.	B	44.	E	44.	B
45.	D	45.	B	45.	B	45.	E
46.	C	46.	C	46.	E	46.	C
47.	A	47.	A	47.	D	47.	B
48.	D	48.	D	48.	E	48.	C
49.	B	49.	A	49.	A	49.	D
50.	C	50.	C	50.	C	50.	A
51.	B	51.	D	51.	B		
52.	C	52.	E	52.	D		
53.	D	53.	E	53.	C		
54.	A	54.	C	54.	B		
		55.	D	55.	C		
		56.	B	56.	D		
		57.	C	57.	C		
		58.	C	58.	E		
				59.	C		
				60.	B		

CHAPTER 5		CHAPTER 6		CHAPTER 7		CHAPTER 8	
1.	C	1.	B	1.	A	1.	B
2.	A	2.	C	2.	B	2.	D
3.	D	3.	B	3.	A	3.	C
4.	E	4.	B	4.	C	4.	D
5.	C	5.	D	5.	A	5.	E
6.	B	6.	C	6.	D	6.	D
7.	C	7.	D	7.	B	7.	C
8.	D	8.	B	8.	E	8.	D
9.	C	9.	A	9.	A	9.	B
10.	D	10.	D	10.	B	10.	A
11.	E	11.	C	11.	C	11.	C
12.	D	12.	C	12.	B	12.	A
13.	C	13.	D	13.	C	13.	C
14.	D	14.	B	14.	B	14.	E
15.	A	15.	D	15.	D	15.	A
16.	D	16.	D	16.	A	16.	A
17.	C	17.	B	17.	C	17.	C
18.	A	18.	C	18.	C	18.	C
19.	A	19.	A	19.	B	19.	C
20.	C	20.	A	20.	C	20.	D
21.	B	21.	B	21.	D	21.	D
22.	D	22.	B	22.	B	22.	B
23.	C	23.	B	23.	C	23.	C
24.	A	24.	A	24.	A	24.	B
25.	B	25.	D	25.	D	25.	B
26.	C	26.	C	26.	D	26.	B
27.	B	27.	B	27.	B	27.	A
28.	B	28.	A	28.	B	28.	C
29.	A	29.	D	29.	C	29.	D
30.	A	30.	C	30.	D	30.	D
31.	C	31.	D	31.	B	31.	A
32.	B	32.	D	32.	A	32.	B
33.	D	33.	D	33.	C	33.	E
34.	B	34.	B	34.	B	34.	D
35.	D	35.	B	35.	A	35.	D
36.	C	36.	D	36.	D	36.	D
37.	A	37.	B	37.	E	37.	D
38.	B	38.	C	38.	A	38.	B
39.	D	39.	B	39.	B	39.	B
40.	C	40.	D	40.	C	40.	A
41.	C	41.	B	41.	C	41.	C
42.	C	42.	B	42.	B	42.	C
43.	C	43.	C	43.	D	43.	B
44.	D	44.	C	44.	B	44.	B
45.	C	45.	D	45.	D	45.	C
46.	E	46.	B	46.	D	46.	B
47.	A	47.	C			47.	B
48.	B	48.	C			48.	B
49.	D	49.	C			49.	C
		50.	B			50.	E
		51.	B				
		52.	C				

CHAPTER 9		CHAPTER 10		CHAPTER 11		CHAPTER 12	
1.	A	1.	D	1.	B	1.	C
2.	B	2.	B	2.	C	2.	A
3.	A	3.	C	3.	E	3.	B
4.	C	4.	A	4.	D	4.	D
5.	B	5.	B	5.	A	5.	E
6.	D	6.	C	6.	A	6.	C
7.	D	7.	C	7.	B	7.	A
8.	A	8.	B	8.	D	8.	E
9.	A	9.	B	9.	C	9.	B
10.	C	10.	A	10.	B	10.	B
11.	A	11.	A	11.	C	11.	D
12.	B	12.	B	12.	D	12.	D
13.	C	13.	D	13.	A	13.	A
14.	B	14.	C	14.	C	14.	C
15.	D	15.	B	15.	B	15.	D
16.	C	16.	D	16.	C	16.	B
17.	B	17.	A	17.	B	17.	A
18.	C	18.	C	18.	C	18.	C
19.	C	19.	D	19.	C	19.	A
20.	A	20.	C	20.	A	20.	D
21.	E	21.	D	21.	B	21.	E
22.	C	22.	D	22.	B	22.	A
23.	C	23.	D	23.	B	23.	D
24.	A	24.	B	24.	C	24.	A
25.	C	25.	D	25.	C	25.	A
26.	E	26.	B	26.	D	26.	B
27.	B	27.	C	27.	C	27.	C
28.	B	28.	B	28.	B	28.	D
29.	A	29.	C	29.	C	29.	D
30.	B	30.	A	30.	A	30.	A
31.	C			31.	C		
32.	A			32.	D		
33.	D			33.	C		
34.	A			34.	B		
35.	C			35.	A		
36.	D			36.	E		
37.	B						
38.	D						
39.	A						
40.	D						

CHAPTER 13	CHAPTER 14	CHAPTER 15	CHAPTER 16
1. B	1. C	1. C	1. B
2. A	2. B	2. D	2. B
3. D	3. D	3. A	3. A
4. C	4. A	4. B	4. B
5. A	5. D	5. D	5. B
6. C	6. A	6. C	6. A
7. D	7. C	7. A	7. C
8. C	8. B	8. C	8. B
9. D	9. D	9. B	9. C
10. C	10. A	10. A	10. A
11. A	11. D	11. B	11. C
12. A	12. A	12. E	12. C
13. B	13. E	13. E	13. B
14. B	14. C	14. A	14. C
15. A	15. B	15. C	15. C
16. E	16. B	16. C	16. B
17. C	17. C	17. E	17. B
18. B	18. B	18. A	18. A
19. A	19. B	19. C	19. A
20. B	20. B	20. A	20. A
21. C	21. C	21. C	21. A
22. D	22. C	22. D	22. C
23. D	23. B	23. A	23. C
24. A	24. A	24. D	24. A
25. C	25. D	25. B	25. B
26. B	26. A	26. B	26. D
27. B	27. B	27. A	27. B
28. C	28. C	28. D	28. B
29. A	29. B	29. D	29. B
30. C	30. C	30. A	30. C
31. D	31. C	31. C	31. A
32. C	32. D	32. A	32. C
33. D	33. D	33. B	33. B
34. A	34. D	34. D	34. D
35. B	35. B	35. B	35. B
36. B	36. D	36. C	36. A
37. C	37. D	37. B	37. D
38. D	38. C	38. B	38. A
39. B	39. A	39. C	39. D
40. C	40. C	40. A	40. A
		41. B	41. B
		42. A	42. A
		43. C	43. B
		44. B	44. B
		45. B	45. C
		46. C	46. D
		47. D	47. A
		48. A	48. B
		49. A	49. D
		50. A	50. B
		51. E	
		52. B	